The Geological Society of America
Memoir 72

COASTAL SAND DUNES OF OREGON AND WASHINGTON

By

WILLIAM S. COOPER

Boulder, Colorado

June 18, 1958

PRINTED BY WAVERLY PRESS, INC.
BALTIMORE, MD.

PUBLISHED BY THE GEOLOGICAL SOCIETY OF AMERICA
Address all communications to the Geological Society of America
419 West 117 Street, New York 27, N. Y.

ACKNOWLEDGMENTS

Three institutions have been generous in financial aid in connection with the present work. Numerous grants have been received from the faculty research fund of the Graduate School, University of Minnesota, which have been applied to field expenses for myself and my assistants, the making of aerophotos, and miscellaneous uses. The American Philosophical Society, through its Penrose Fund, aided in the making of the first extensive set of aerophotos. A second set was made possible by a grant from the Penrose Bequest of The Geological Society of America, which in part was applied also to preparation of the manuscript. The University of Minnesota, in addition to financial aid, awarded me a summer research appointment, which was given to organization of materials. To these institutions I offer my deep gratitude. I wish also to express my appreciation of the generous grant received from the Works Projects Administration at the University of Minnesota in the years 1940–1942 for translation of publications in foreign languages. Copies of all translations have been filed with the American Documentation Institute, Washington, D. C.

I wish to acknowledge the efficient work done by my field assistants: Dr. Frank E. Egler in 1933, Mr. John Hall in 1940, and Dr. John W. Marr in 1941. Several supplemental studies have been made for me. Mr. C. O. Morgan of Winchester Bay, Oregon, carried out a 6-year series of measurements of dune movement and made lake soundings. Mr. K. N. Phillips, Dr. and Mrs. Donald B. Lawrence, Mr. Len Ramp, Dr. John W. Marr, and Dr. Quentin D. Clarkson have visited various dune localities to clear up points that in preparation of the manuscript presented elements of uncertainty. Credit is given for these in the text. I am grateful to Mr. Emil Peterson of North Bend, Oregon, for helpful guidance in my first exploration of Locality 23, Coos Bay dune sheet.

I am grateful to the following men for reading and criticizing the manuscript or parts of it: Dr. Ewart M. Baldwin, University of Oregon; Mr. Robert L. Brown, U. S. Soil Conservation Service; Dr. Richard Foster Flint, Yale University; Dr. W. C. Krumbein, Northwestern University; Mr. T. T. Munger and his associates in the Pacific Northwest Forest and Range Experiment Station; Dr. R. P. Sharp, California Institute of Technology; Dr. H. T. U. Smith, University of Massachusetts; Dr. K. D. Wood, University of Colorado; and Dr. H. E. Wright, University of Minnesota. Other individuals who have given valuable information are Dr. H. P. Hansen, Oregon State College; Mr. Emil Peterson, North Bend, Oregon; Dr. L. G. Straub, University of Minnesota; Mr. Francisco Flores, Lisbon, Portugal; Chief of the Siuslaw Coast Guard Station, Oregon; Keeper of the Umpqua Lighthouse, Oregon; and the U. S. Army Corps of Engineers, Portland, Oregon, District, Oregon State Fish and Game Commission, Oregon State Highway Department.

CONTENTS

ILLUSTRATIONS

TABLES

ABSTRACT

In Part I the environment of the coastal dunes of Oregon and Washington is analyzed. Most of the substratum is a narrow foreland or terrace, in part submerged, that borders the mountain front. Temperature is relatively low in summer and rarely reaches the freezing point in winter. Winter precipitation is heavy, and there is almost no snow; there is a pronounced deficiency in precipitation in summer. The summer wind is a very constant afternoon sea breeze from north to northwest; winter winds are variable but include frequent southwest gales. Longshore currents are governed by the seasonal winds, moving southward in summer and northward in winter. The regional vegetation is dense, tall conifer forest. The influence of man has been comparatively slight: in prehistoric times the starting of forest fires; in historic time moderate disturbance due to grazing and recent efforts to control the movement of the sand.

Part II deals with forms and processes. The simplest combination of elements comprises sand, wind, and water. Interaction of these produces two patterns. In the transverse-ridge pattern the individual unit is a ridge essentially normal to the summer wind and moving with it; it is asymmetric in profile with gentle windward slope and steep leeward slope (slipface). Origin and maintenance of this profile are explained in accordance with principles developed in the field of aerodynamics, and conclusions arrived at deductively are confirmed by slow-motion photography of smoke streams on the dunes.

The oblique-ridge pattern occurs only where there is full exposure to both seasonal winds, plenty of space, and plenty of sand. These conditions are met only in Region III (Coos Bay dune sheet). The units are much more massive than the transverse ridges and are essentially stationary. Their trend lies between the means of summer and winter winds. A theoretical explanation of their origin and maintenance is presented, and the oblique ridges and the "longitudinal dunes" of certain desert regions are compared. Neither transverse nor oblique ridge is found in stabilized condition.

The factor vegetation added to the other three—sand, wind, and water—promotes stabilization. On a prograding shore, successive beach ridges are quickly captured and fixed, and retain their initial form indefinitely. On a retrograding shore the processes are exceedingly complex and involve repeated stabilization and rejuvenation. Two cases are presented: flat shore, with and without abundant sand supply; stabilized dune masses undergoing erosion. In the latter case, the commoner, development involves the following phases: trough blowout, merging of troughs, reduction to deflation base, and precipitation ridge, which may in time become completely stabilized while still retaining its characteristic form. In places sheltered from one or the other of the seasonal winds, usually the summer wind, giant parabola dunes, which may likewise become fixed by vegetation, develop.

Part III is a description of the dune localities of the Oregon-Washington coast and an account of their history. Forty per cent of this coast bears dunes of greater or lesser magnitude. Thirty dune localities are grouped in four regions. Region I includes four localities north of Tillamook Head, Oregon, making a continuous strip 53 km long, that bears the parallel beach-dune-ridge pattern associated with progradation. The forms in Regions II, III, and IV, heterogeneous and complex, are those characteristic of retrograding shores. The two principal stabilized forms are the precipitation ridge and the parabola dune.

In Regions II, III, and IV the existing features came into being mainly during the last grand period of sea-level rise, and the seaward portions of massive parabola complexes have been sliced away in varying degree by the advancing sea. The

1

beach-ridge dunes of Region I were formed during the period of comparatively stable sea level, with a probable small net lowering, which followed the maximum of sea advance and has extended to the present. Progradation here during this period, in contrast with almost none south of Tillamook Head, has been possible because of the ample bed load carried to the coast by the Columbia River.

South of Tillamook Head there is, in a number of well-distributed localities, evidence of three episodes of advance. The first is represented by the strip of thoroughly stabilized dunes that nearly everywhere forms the inner marginal part of the dune complexes. This episode reached its culmination before the sea had attained its maximum of advance—attested by the slicing away of portions of completely stabilized masses. The second advance for the most part fell short of the first, though in a few places it overpassed the limits of the latter; present condition ranges from complete stabilization to vigorous activity. The third episode is represented by active dunes with open access to the shore. In certain localities there are only an inner strip of stabilized dunes and an outer zone of active dunes. It is assumed that in these the visible effects of the second and third episodes have merged.

An earlier cycle of dune development, similar to the modern one in character and extent, is proved by eolian sediments containing altered podzolic soils, which make a minor part of the mantle of unconsolidated materials that lies upon the rock platform of the 30-m terrace. The dunes of which these masses are remnants were formed during the next-to-the-last grand period of submergence.

Development of the dunes of Regions II, III, and IV, associated with the grand period of submergence, is assigned to the period of deglaciation that followed the Wisconsin maximum, and mainly to the period of rapid deglaciation that began after the Valders-Mankato advance. The beach-ridge dunes of Region I, on the other hand, have developed in their entirety in the time since sea-level rise was succeeded by stability. By analogy, the earlier cycle of dune development was associated with the waning phase of Illinoian glaciation, and it may be assumed that similar dune cycles were associated with the earlier glaciations of the Pleistocene.

INTRODUCTION

DISTRIBUTION OF DUNES ON THE PACIFIC COAST OF NORTH AMERICA

Sand dunes occur at irregular intervals along the entire Pacific coast of North America. Because of the steep, rugged nature of this coast they are less continuous and cover a far lesser frontage than on the Atlantic side of the continent, but in many localities they are massive and complex.

On the south coast of Alaska there are dune areas of considerable magnitude. Those of the Copper River delta, which the writer has visited briefly, are sufficiently active so that the Copper River Railroad found it necessary to build sand sheds to prevent drifting on the tracks. The fiord coast of southeastern Alaska and British Columbia is inhospitable to surf-borne sand, and the writer knows of no important dunes upon it.

The largest percentage of dune frontage is found on the regular, gently concave coast between Cape Flattery and Cape Blanco. South of Cape Blanco, all the way to the Golden Gate, dune masses are comparatively small and widely separated. There are localities of interest at Point St. George, Humboldt Bay, Point Arena, and Bodega Head. Just south of the Golden Gate there was once a wide expanse of dunes, now completely obliterated. The shore of Monterey Bay is bordered by a dune complex of more than ordinary extent and significance. Next in order is an interesting area at Morro Bay near San Luis Obispo. The most extensive and complex dune masses of the California coast lie north and south of the Santa Maria River and Point Sal; they have a combined frontage of 36 km. The southernmost dune mass of the ocean coast studied by the writer is imposing and is at Socorro, Baja California (30° 20′ N. Lat.). One dune locality, Libertad, on the Gulf coast of Sonora a little farther south than Socorro, has been visited.

DUNES OF THE OREGON-WASHINGTON COAST: LOCATION AND GENERAL CHARACTER

Of the total ocean-facing coast line of Oregon, approximately 500 km long (ignoring minor features), 225 km, or 45 per cent, bears dunes of greater or lesser magnitude. The dune areas are rather evenly distributed except at the extreme south; beyond Cape Blanco they are few and small. In Washington the extent of dune-bordered shore line is 82 km or 31 per cent of the distance between Cape Flattery and the Columbia River. Here the dune areas are concentrated in a continuous strip constituting the southern third of the coast line; north of this there are almost no dunes. In inland extension the dune masses are extremely variable, ranging from a mere fringe to maxima of 4.5 km in Oregon and 3.1 km in Washington.

There are four natural groups of localities, based upon distinctive features in common. The localities of Region I (three in Washington, one in Oregon) are unique in their series of ridges parallel to the shore, characteristic of prograding coasts. All the others bear the marks of destruction associated with retrogradation. In Region II, eight localities provide a remarkable series exhibiting progressive stages in truncation of formerly more extensive dune masses. Region III, the Coos Bay dune sheet, is actually a single unit—a strip of dunes 86 km long broken only by the mouths of the Siuslaw and Umpqua rivers and a few minor streams. This is the most continuous and widest of the dune areas and furnishes the most comprehensive display of forms and processes. The principal feature in Region IV is a lengthy strip of well-developed dunes north and south of the Coquille River.

The dune localities are numbered from 1 at the north to 30 at the south. They are shown on the map (Pl. 1), and a list is given below. The designations are derived from coast features, mainly bays and rivers, to which the dunes are related.

REGION I. Columbia River
  (Washington)
    1. Grays Harbor North
    2. Grays Harbor South
    3. Willapa Bay
  (Oregon)
    4. Clatsop Plains
REGION II. Northern Oregon
    5. Nehalem River
    6. Rockaway
    7. Tillamook Bay
    8. Netarts Bay
    9. Sand Lake
  10. Nestucca Bay
  11. Neskowin Creek
  12. Salmon River
  13. Devil's Lake
  14. Siletz Bay.

  15. Yaquina Bay
  16. Alsea Bay
  17. Tenmile Creek
  18. China Creek
REGION III. Coos Bay Dune Sheet
  19. Siuslaw River North
  20. Siuslaw River South
  21. Umpqua River North
  22. Umpqua River South
  23. Coos Bay
REGION IV. Southern Oregon
  24. Coquille River North
  25. Coquille River South
  26. Fourmile Creek
  27. Sixes River
  28. Elk River
  29. Euchre Creek
  30. Pistol River

STATUS OF DUNE RESEARCH

GENERAL

The literature on sand dunes is of enormous extent, and all but a small part has been produced in Europe. This is quite natural for several reasons. In a comparatively small country bordering the sea almost everyone is aware of coastal phenomena, and, in particular, coastal sand dunes assume roles of great economic importance. In many places they are a menace to man's activities and must be controlled; in some; actual use has been successfully joined with restraint. It is not surprising that Germany, with the most extensive and varied array of coastal dunes, has produced the largest body of literature. French investigations of maritime dunes have been concentrated on the very important ones of the Gascon coast. Significant papers have come from Denmark, Holland, and Belgium. Holland, in particular, has had compelling reasons for intensive dune study. In other parts of the world there have been studies of coastal dunes in Australia, New Zealand, and Argentina. In most of these investigations, emphasis—in some cases undue emphasis—has been laid upon plants as agents in dune processes, which is natural enough, since almost all the work has been done on coasts under moist climates and since plants are the only effective means of artificial control.

A few works that are general in scope should be cited. The earliest comprehensive work on sand dunes is probably that by Sokolow (Russian 1884, German translation 1894); it covers continental as well as maritime dunes. Jentsch (1900) contributed the geological part to Gerhardt's "Handbuch des Dünenbaues," and Solger (1910) to

"Dünenbuch." Braun (1911) presented a survey of European lowland coasts and their dunes.

In the field of desert dunes the principal studies have been made in the various subdivisions of the Sahara. The western part has been covered by French investigators, the eastern by British. Outstanding among the latter is Bagnold, whose comprehensive work on the physics of blown sand (1941), based on experiment and on long field experience in Egypt and Libya, is the most important contribution in its field. Other desert regions where investigations of dune phenomena have been carried on are central Asia (Hedin, 1896; 1904) and central Australia (Madigan, 1936; 1946). The dunes of Peru, which may be classed as both desert and coastal, have been superficially described (Bowman, 1916; 1924; H. T. U. Smith, 1954). Other great dune-covered deserts, such as that of Arabia, have barely been touched. In some continental interiors there are numerous dune fields not related to true desert conditions. For Europe these have been mapped by H. T. U. Smith (personal communication); the most extensive are those of Hungary (Cholnoky, 1902). Those of Germany, Poland, and Scandinavia date from the last deglaciation and have long been stabilized (for a brief survey *see* Cooper, 1935, p. 104–108).

NORTH AMERICA

Here the list of important contributions is meager. The coastal dunes have been particularly neglected, although they cover a great extent of shore line and in many places are imposing. The impact of coastal phenomena upon the people has been far less than in such a country as Germany or Holland, and the danger from dune encroachment has been exceedingly small in comparison with the coasts of Europe. No studies have been made that can be considered either intensive or comprehensive from the standpoint of geomorphology. Plant ecologists have produced papers that will be useful when more comprehensive dune investigations are made. Cooper (1936), in a work collateral to the present one, made a geographic study of the strand and dune flora of the Pacific coast of North America. A classic ecological study of the shore dunes of Lake Michigan was made by Cowles (1899), and Cressey (1928) considered them from the geomorphologic standpoint. Landsberg (1942), Landsberg and Riley (1943), and Rossby (1943) reported on a study of wind behavior over a Lake Michigan dune.

Continental dunes have been studied more than coastal dunes in North America, perhaps in part because of stimulation provided by the dust-bowl conditions of the 1930's. Contributions by H. T. U. Smith (1940; 1949; 1951), Melton (1940), Hack (1941), and Cooper (1935; 1938) should be cited. Rapid increase of interest in eolian phenomena in North America is indicated by the recent publication of a map of the Pleistocene eolian deposits of the continent (Geol. Soc. America, 1952; *see* also Thorp and Smith, 1949).

COAST OF OREGON AND WASHINGTON

Here, the number of studies is extremely small. Diller (1895–1896) described the parallel ridges of the Clatsop Plains and in the Coos Bay Geologic Folio (1901) made brief mention of the dunes included therein. House (1914a; 1914b; 1918) published popular descriptions of the dunes of the Coos Bay region and their vegetation. Warren D. Smith (1933), in a physiographic survey of the Oregon coast, treated the dunes briefly, giving special attention to the Clatsop Plains. Egler (1934) reported on the plant communities and successional trends on the dunes of the Coos Bay region. The present writer, in a progress report to the American Philosophical Society (Cooper, 1944), summarized aspects of his work dealing with the aerodynamics of the dunes. He also contributed a brief popular account of the dunes to a history of Coos and Curry Counties, Oregon (Peterson and Powers, 1952).

PRESENT WORK
INCEPTION AND DEVELOPMENT

The present work arose from a projected plant-ecological study of the coastal dunes of California. The dunes themselves, however, almost immediately assumed first place, and plants were relegated to the important role of geologic agent. A systematic survey of the dune areas from below the Mexican boundary to Puget Sound resulted in selection of the Coos Bay dune sheet in Oregon for intensive investigation of dune phenomena. The field was later extended to include the entire coast of Oregon and Washington.

Field work was carried on during portions of the summers of 1925, 1928, 1933, 1940, and 1941. The Coos Bay dune sheet was examined in minute detail, and experimental studies were carried on there. For the other dune areas less intensive study was required, particularly when coverage by aerial photography became feasible. After preliminary use of this method had proved its great value, a complete aerial survey of the Coos Bay dune sheet was made in September 1940, and April 1941. Certain areas were photographed on both flights for comparison of dry-season and wet-season conditions. The scale was approximately 1:16,000, or 1 km = 6.25 cm. A second partial survey was made in September 1953 to permit determination of changes that had occurred since 1940 and for other purposes.[1] For other dune areas there were available aerophotos made by Government agencies: for the Oregon coast, Corps of Engineers, U. S. Army; for Washington, U. S. Coast and Geodetic Survey and U. S. Air Force. Drawing upon all these sources, complete aerial coverage was attained. Equally complete was map coverage by topographic sheets of the U. S. Geological Survey and Army Corps of Engineers.

Distance scales and directions as indicated on the aerophotos and tracings from them are the closest possible approximations. For the Coos Bay dune sheet ground measurements between points indentifiable on the aerophotos were made in each locality, and distances are based on these. The mosaics have only approximate ground control based on the topographic maps. Hundreds of altitude determinations by aneroid were made with a Tycos instrument reading to 2 feet. Check readings at known points were made as frequently as possible, and an error curve was constructed for each day's observations. No undue reliance has been placed upon these readings.

---

[1] The first photographic survey was made by Brubaker Aerial Surveys of Portland, the second by Delano Aerial Surveys of the same city.

FUNDAMENTAL VIEWPOINT

The fundamental viewpoint in this work is that in degree of importance process comes before form. In the first part the attempt is made to discover the processes through which the dune forms of this coast come into being and develop; in the second the object is to trace the larger, historical processes whereby the dune masses and complexes have attained their present state.

Numerous attempts have been made to define the word "dune." So far as precision is concerned, all have failed.[2] The very general concept expressed by the dictionary definition—"a hill or ridge of sand piled up by the wind"—is, however, a useful one. There is an infinite variety of such "hills of sand," from which emerge a small number of types sufficiently definite and widespread to have acquired serviceable designations. A number of authors have tried to combine them in systems of classification. Some of these are built upon a hypothetical genetic foundation, in which a single dune form, regarded as "primitive," "fundamental," or "ideal," gives rise to all the others. Two rather elaborate classifications are those of Van Dieren (1934) and Melton (1940). The former has devised for his system a complete Latin terminology. No attempt is here made to classify dune forms either statically or genetically or to devise a system of terminology; it is my belief that classifications and terminologies are means toward an end, not ends in themselves, and should be held to the minimum necessary for clearness. Introduction of a few new terms and expressions has been unavoidable, and these are defined where first used.

I feel that too often a sharp distinction has been made between coastal and desert dunes. The two groups have many fundamentals in common, and I hope to show that sounder progress may be made through study of these common features than by stressing the differences between them.

A sincere effort has been made to avoid provinciality—the assumption that conclusions reached in a particular region must apply everywhere. The work is frankly a regional study; but such a study is relatively sterile if it does not yield concepts that may prove to have wide application. Certain suggestions to that end have been made—it is hoped with the proper degree of humility. It is up to students in other regions to test their validity. In order to facilitate such tests, presentation of the environment of the dunes is made full and detailed. It has been found that lack of such background in certain otherwise excellent works has made comparison difficult and uncertain.

---

[2] A recent attempt is that of Bagnold (1941, p. 188): "True Dunes. A single dune may be defined as a mound or hill of sand which rises to a single summit. Dunes may exist alone or attached to one another in colonies or dune chains." An undulating dune ridge, according to this definition, has no right to existence as a concrete entity, but is a combination of theoretical units corresponding to its high points, which shift their positions from time to time and are not necessarily related genetically to discrete embryonic units.

PART I: ENVIRONMENT OF THE DUNES

GEOMORPHIC FEATURES OF THE COAST REGION

OREGON

The coastal strip of Oregon is continuously mountainous. The Oregon Coast Range stretches from the Columbia River southward to about the latitude of Cape Blanco. It consists of Tertiary sedimentary and volcanic rocks; in structure it is a broad, low anticlinorium (Fenneman, 1931). South of Cape Blanco, extending into California, are the Klamath Mountains, merging topographically with the Coast Range but older in materials and more complex in structure. For long distances the mountain front is at the shore; at no point is it more than 6 km inland. In the Coast Range portion initial rise of the mountain mass is to about 300 m, in the Klamath region twice as great. The space between the mountain front and the shore is occupied by a narrow, interrupted strip of terrace nature.

From the Columbia River to Cape Blanco the coast line takes the form of a very gentle arc; the northern portion trends almost exactly south, and curvature increases southward. The regularity of this part of the coast is due mainly to truncation of mountain masses and terraces by the advancing sea. Continuity is made almost complete by spits, bay bars, and other sand masses deposited by longshore currents and waves across the mouths of drowned river valleys and in re-entrants. At rather frequent intervals from the Columbia River to Cape Blanco occur promontories with high sea cliffs, nearly all of them masses of igneous rock more resistant than the neighboring sedimentary rocks. They do not extend far into the ocean; the most striking is Cape Lookout, a narrow wedge projecting 3 km due west. From Cape Blanco to the California line the trend of the coast is south-south-east. Most of the shore line is rocky and much less regular in detail; bars and spits are small and scarce.

The region of the Coast Range was peneplaned in post-Miocene time, the Klamath region perhaps earlier (Diller, 1902; Maxson, 1932); unreduced volcanic masses remained as monadnocks. The history since peneplanation has been characterized by ups and downs of considerable magnitude (Diller, 1901; 1902; 1903). During a period of submergence, probably in late Pliocene or early Pleistocene time, sea level stood at least 450 m higher on the land than at present; terrace fragments occur at this level. Emergence followed, several times interrupted; the reversal of trend is proved by terrace remnants at successively lower levels. No comprehensive investigation of these terraces and the events associated with them has yet been made. More or less general descriptions have been provided by Diller (1901; 1902; 1903), W. D. Smith (1933), Pardee (1934), Twenhofel (1943; 1946), Allen and Baldwin (1944), and Baldwin (1945). Griggs (1945) has made a fairly detailed study of a limited area north and south of the Coquille River.

The lower terraces are of some consequence in this study, since they form the substratum for most of the dune masses. Strict correlation is at present not possible, but observation indicates that there is one terrace that is more distinct and continuous than the rest and which constitutes the shelf that borders the mountain front over lengthy portions of the coast. For long distances its inner margin stands at about 30

9

m; since it has, however, been deformed it rises to more than 60 m in some places and descends to sea level or below in others (Baldwin, 1945). It may conveniently be termed the "30-meter terrace." Its continuity is frequently broken by rocky headlands and at river mouths. In width it ranges from a mere trace to more than 3 km. For at least half its extent it is faced with a cliff or bluff, which in some places is being actively eroded by the surf, whereas in others there is a beach below. At a number of places where the foreland extends back into re-entrants in the mountain front there is no cliff; the surface slopes to sea level and passes beneath it. In such a situation the actual shore lies farther out, at the seaward margin of a barrier comprising beach and dunes, behind which there are in some cases lagoons and even lakes of considerable size. Downwarping may of course produce the same effect, and the choice in certain cases is in doubt. Baldwin (1945, p. 36) admits that relatively greater distance from the shore may cause drowning of the foreland surface but believes that warping is the primary cause.

The rock platform of the terrace bears a layer of unconsolidated materials, variable in thickness. Whereas the rock platform is the only authentic criterion for correlation of terrace levels, it is the surface of the mantle layer that is of primary importance for the dunes, since they rest directly upon it. The mantle was named the "Elk River beds" by Diller (1902, p. 31), and the term has been defined more precisely by Baldwin (1945, p. 42) as applying to "all the terrace deposits forming this terrace along the Oregon coast." The materials are dominantly marine in origin, but there are many bodies that are clearly eolian. The latter, which will be discussed in a later section, must be sharply distinguished from the modern dunes.

Dissection of the terrace is at a very youthful stage. Streams coming from the mountains naturally have trenched it; ravines tributary to these are short. Large areas are almost intact.

In certain localities there is evidence of a higher, older terrace—possibly more than one—with a mantle similar to the first and containing the same sort of eolian material as a minor component. The two most conspicuous areas are in Locality 20, from the Siuslaw River to Siltcoos Lake, and in Locality 22. The topography in these is distinguished from that of the 30-m terrace not only in altitude but in its far more advanced stage of dissection. The present study is not concerned with higher terrace levels than these.

WASHINGTON

The southern half of the coast region of Washington is a rolling plain lying between the Coast Range, which is decidedly less prominent than in Oregon, and the ocean. Terrace levels along the coast and rivers have not been seriously investigated. The equivalent of the Elk River beds is present, and shore bluffs have been cut in it north of Grays Harbor. Further details are available in Arnold (1906), Lupton (1915), Glover (1940), Baldwin (1945), and Lowry and Baldwin (1952).

The most conspicuous single features are two deeply penetrating indentations: Grays Harbor and Willapa Bay with its southern branch, Shoalwater Bay (Pl. 1). The peninsulas that bound them on the ocean side, and the adjoining forelands are intimately involved with dune history.

CLIMATE

GENERAL CHARACTER

The Köppen designation gives adequate expression to the features of the climate: the formula is *Csb*, in which *C* is mesothermal, *s* is summer-dry, *b* is median temperature within *C*. Ackerman (1941) has attempted a more precise characterization by use of the expression *Csmb*, in which *m* signifies sufficient precipitation to compensate

TABLE 1.—*Average monthly and annual temperature for four stations on the Washington-Oregon coast*

Fahrenheit. Data from U. S. Weather Bureau

	Length of record, (years)	Jan.	Feb.	Mar.	April	May	June	July	Aug.	Sept.	Oct.	Nov.	Dec.	Annual
North Head Lat. 46° 18′	65	42.1	43.0	45.2	47.5	50.9	54.8	57.2	57.6	56.5	52.9	48.2	44.1	50.0
Tillamook Lat. 45° 29′	46	42.5	44.3	45.7	48.4	52.0	55.8	58.8	58.9	56.4	52.9	47.9	44.0	50.6
Newport Lat. 44° 38′	57	43.8	45.2	46.3	48.9	51.9	55.4	57.0	57.5	56.3	53.6	49.0	45.4	50.9
North Bend Lat. 43° 25′	50	44.2	45.8	47.5	49.7	52.9	56.4	59.4	60.1	58.1	54.1	49.6	45.0	51.9

for the short dry season. The region is intermediate between *Cfb* to the north, with no period of precipitation deficiency, and *Cs* to the south, with a long, almost rainless summer season. Thornthwaite in his first essay (1931) places it in *AC'r*, where *A* is wet, *C'* is microthermal, *r* is precipitation at all seasons. In his second study (1948), making no attempt to integrate the symbols he uses into a single expression, he characterizes the region as mesothermal with low summer concentration of thermal efficiency and perhumid with little or no water deficiency in any season.

TEMPERATURE

Table 1 and Figure 1*A* present data for four stations: North Head, Washington; and Tillamook, Newport, and North Bend, evenly spaced on the Oregon coast between the Columbia River and Cape Blanco. The curves for the four stations are very similar and the differences associated with latitude are insignificant. The spread between warmest and coldest months is small: at North Head and Newport, fully exposed to coastal influences, it is 15.5° F. and 13.7° F. respectively. At Tillamook and North Bend, somewhat removed from oceanic influences, it is slightly greater: 16.4° and 15.9°. Freezing temperatures are infrequent and transitory.

PRECIPITATION

The patterns for the four stations (Table 2; Fig. 1*B*) are similar: heavy winter precipitation and a definite summer deficiency culminating in July and August. In summer most of the storm tracks pass farther north; the winter rains are brought by cyclonic storms, whose tracks shift southward during this season. Total precipitation at a given station varies greatly from year to year. Snow falls occasionally but is insignificant in amount and quickly vanishes

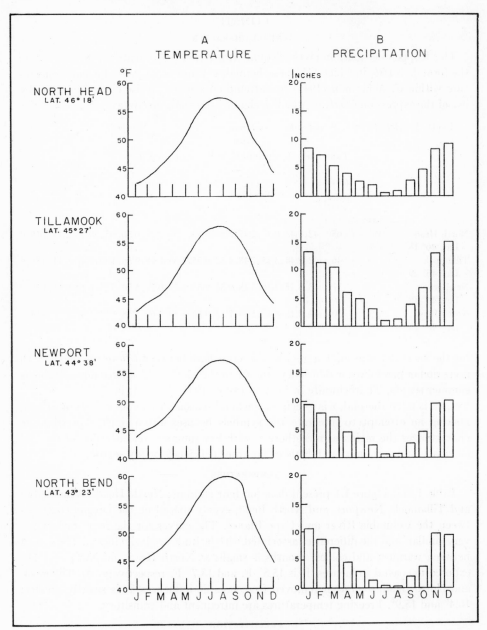

FIGURE 1.—*Annual march of temperature and precipitation at four stations on the Washington-Oregon coast*

HUMIDITY, CLOUD, AND FOG

Quantitative data pertaining to these climatic elements are, as usual, scanty. Observational data taken at the Siuslaw Coast Guard Station, Oregon, for 1 year are presented in Table 3. Clear days are infrequent throughout the year. Days that are cloudy or have both cloud and fog without rain occur frequently at all seasons. Fog alone is very common from June through September. Frequency of rainy days is inversely proportional to that of foggy days. It may be assumed that humidity is

TABLE 2.—*Average monthly and annual precipitation for four stations on the Washington-Oregon coast*

Inches. Data from U. S. Weather Bureau

	Length of record (years)	Jan.	Feb.	Mar.	April	May	June	July	Aug.	Sept.	Oct.	Nov.	Dec.	An-nual	Snow
North Head Lat. 46° 18′	75	8.78	7.45	5.56	4.14	2.95	2.28	0.96	1.05	2.99	5.01	8.45	9.48	59.10	..
Tillamook Lat. 45° 29′	42	13.48	11.59	10.74	6.36	5.17	3.16	1.33	1.48	4.18	7.28	13.51	15.22	93.50	5.4
Newport Lat. 44° 38′	58	9.70	8.06	7.45	4.60	3.50	2.55	0.78	0.91	2.77	4.87	9.98	10.64	65.81	1.6
North Bend Lat. 43° 25′	51	10.90	8.89	7.54	4.96	3.22	1.68	0.49	0.39	2.40	4.08	9.95	9.79	64.13	1.9

TABLE 3.—*Number of days with cloud, fog, and rain at Siuslaw Coast Guard Station, Oregon*

September 1939, through August 1940.

	Clear	Cloudy	Cloud and fog	Fog	Rain
1939 September	6	4	8	12	....
October	5	9	7	4	6
November	3	9	10	2	6
December	....	9	7	....	15
1940 January	3	14	5	....	9
February	....	6	5	1	17
March	6	10	5	....	10
April	2	23	4	....	1
May	5	9	7	6	4
June	8	2	7	13	....
July	4	15	6	6	....
August	5	5	7	14	....
Year	47	115	78	58	68

high throughout the year. High humidity was vividly demonstrated one August day in 1940. During a hard north-northwesterly wind the sand suddenly became dark in color and its texture coarser. Examination showed that the grains were adhering, making crumbs. Condensation occurred on all surfaces—camera, clothing, hands— and blowing sand stuck to these moist surfaces. After the sand had begun to darken, fog drifted over the top of the high dunes and soon covered the whole area; at no time, however, did it rest on the sand surface.

WIND

Records from weather stations.—In any study of sand dunes wind is obviously the most important climatic element. Because published climatological summaries are totally inadequate, unpublished data were obtained from the United States Weather Bureau. Three stations were selected, evenly spaced along the coast under study: North Head, Washington, and Newport and North Bend, Oregon. The periods of record differ somewhat and are rather short, but these deficiencies are compensated by frequency of observations. The North Head station is on a rocky promontory, 60 m above the sea, immediately north of the mouth of the Columbia River and at the south end of Locality 3. Of the three it is the most exposed. Newport is located on a narrow dune-covered terrace less than 1 km from the shore, and the mountain front is immediately behind. It is the most representative of average dune conditions. The station at North Bend is not so favorably situated, since it lies 5 km from the ocean with hills 50 m and more in height west of it.

The data from the three stations for July and January are presented in Table 4. Wind roses combining frequency and average velocity have been constructed for Newport and North Bend (Fig. 2).[3] Readings of direction and velocity were made every 3 hours; gaps in the record result in an average of seven readings per 24 hours. The frequency figure for direction is the number of times for the whole period of record when a given direction within a given velocity range was recorded. Winds of velocity less than 4 miles per hour are disregarded as being of no importance in dune development. For each station, in the first column of the table and in *A* of the figure, frequency of winds 4 m.p.h. and more is combined with average velocity. In the second column of the table and *B* of the figure, frequency of winds 16 m.p.h. and more, far more important than the gentler winds, is given separately, and the scale on the figure is five times that in *A*.

First consideration is given to July, since summer is the season of greatest dune activity. In frequency of winds 4 m.p.h. and more, all stations agree in overwhelming dominance in the octant N.-NW. At North Head and Newport the highest frequency is north, parallel to the coast; at North Bend (not on the immediate coast) it is also north, but diverging 21° to seaward of the coastal trend. Offshore winds are very infrequent at all stations. With regard to winds 16 m.p.h. and more, all agree in that winds of this velocity are nearly all N.-NW. The highest frequency is N.—parallel to the coast at North Head and Newport, 21° to seaward at North Bend.

Considering average velocities for July, a pronounced maximum is apparent in the northwest quadrant. The highest single value—N. or N.-NW.—is parallel to the coast or one direction unit seaward. At North Head there is a second maximum in the sector S.-SE.—S.-SW., indicated also by the frequency figure for 16 m.p.h. at S.

The month of January, representing winter conditions, presents a sharp contrast to July in almost every respect. Frequency data for winds 4 m.p.h. and more show for all stations a striking preponderance of offshore winds. Analysis shows, however, that these winds are almost all of less than 16 m.p.h. velocity. The figures for winds 16 m.p.h. and more give a very different picture. At Newport the maximum for these

---

[3] The period covered by the data from North Head differs too much from the others to permit fair comparison.

TABLE 4.—*Frequency and velocity of winds at three stations on the Washington-Oregon coast*
July and January

	North Head, Washington Lat. 46°18'			Newport, Oregon Lat. 44°38' 1936–1942			North Bend, Oregon 43°25' 1937–1942		
	Frequency		Av. velocity	Frequency		Av. velocity	Frequency		Av. velocity
	4 m.p.h. and over	16 m.p.h. and over	m.p.h.	4 m.p.h. and over	16 m.p.h. and over	m.p.h.	4 m.p.h. and over	16 m.p.h. and over	m.p.h.
July 1930–1942									
N.	781	410	15.4	389	135	11.9	351	130	12.6
N.-N.E.	15	3	8.4	6	...	4.9	36	2	7.8
N.E.	11	...	5.6	2	...	2.5	37	...	5.2
E.-N.E.	...	...	....	2	...	3.0	2	...	3.3
E.	10	...	5.5	34	...	3.0	6	...	3.1
E.-S.E.	1	...	10.0	11	...	3.8	2	...	3.5
S.E.	44	7	9.2	35	1	3.6	52	...	4.5
S.-S.E.	36	10	13.6	9	...	5.4	20	...	5.3
S.	269	114	14.7	60	5	6.4	24	...	4.3
S.-S.W.	39	14	13.4	48	1	7.9	19	...	7.1
S.W.	129	11	10.1	117	...	6.2	39	...	5.7
W.-S.W.	24	1	7.8	34	...	6.7	19	...	7.5
W.	127	9	8.1	55	...	4.7	16	...	4.8
W.-N.W.	20	2	9.0	27	...	5.6	12	1	7.6
N.W.	437	155	13.1	160	15	7.9	330	70	10.1
N.-N.W.	323	171	15.9	212	60	12.6	172	45	11.3
January 1931–1942									
N.	84	22	11.8	33	3	7.3	28	...	5.4
N.-N.E.	6	...	7.6	6	...	6.4	4	...	6.2
N.E.	61	2	6.0	17	...	5.7	52	1	6.1
E.-N.E.	6	3	9.1	97	...	7.2	5	...	6.0
E.	501	194	13.0	415	6	7.3	19	...	4.8
E.-S.E.	183	110	16.6	160	2	8.5	12	...	4.4
S.E.	383	152	14.3	235	2	6.7	614	5	7.2
S.-S.E.	36	23	19.2	25	4	10.5	149	2	7.3
S.	313	263	27.8	122	59	14.1	114	15	8.9
S.-S.W.	23	23	27.7	46	23	16.1	28	5	12.1
S.W.	125	87	19.9	75	20	11.2	93	23	11.2
W.-S.W.	6	4	15.1	28	10	13.1	7	1	9.9
W.	127	69	16.0	76	7	8.7	12	1	7.2
W.-N.W.	8	5	16.3	17	1	8.1	3	...	5.8
N.W.	118	68	16.8	32	5	9.5	66	9	8.9
N.-N.W.	13	9	18.8	6	...	9.7	11	...	5.3

velocities is S. with lesser frequency seaward to SW. At North Bend the maximum is SW. with lesser frequency landward to S. These winds are clearly of cyclonic nature. North Head has two maxima. One at S. is cyclonic like those of the other stations. The other is at E.-SE. and is due to the pressure gradient from land to sea with

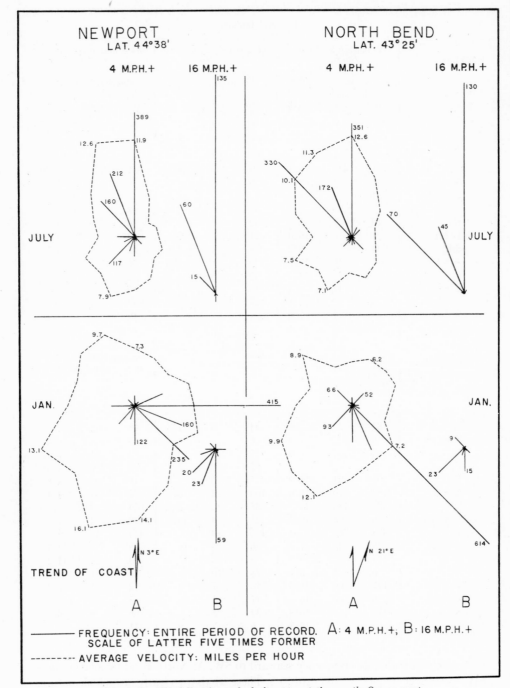

FIGURE 2.—*Wind direction and velocity at two stations on the Oregon coast*

concentration of the wind stream in the Columbia River gorge (Lawrence, 1939). Maximum average velocity in the S.—S.-SW. octant is linked with the maximum frequency for winds 16 m.p.h. and more. These winds are parallel to the coast or slightly to seaward of its trend.

The seasonal wind regime is briefly as follows: In summer, onshore winds greatly predominate, and most of these are confined to the sector N.-NW.; they cover about one octant seaward from the trend of the coast. Winds within this sector have the greatest average velocity. Fall conditions are transitional; winds of the winter type appear in alternation with those of the summer type. In winter, offshore winds are most frequent but have low velocity, except for the gorge winds of the Columbia River. Onshore winds from south to southwest are relatively infrequent but have by far the greatest velocity; they are parallel to the coast or strike it at an acute angle. Spring conditions are again transitional: N.-NW. winds reappear, alternating with the gentle offshore breezes and high-velocity S.-SW. winds of winter.

Observations on the dunes.—Such wind data from weather stations are valuable for painting a generalized picture. Direction data are reliable if the station is situated close to the shore and is without shelter. Velocity data are far from satisfactory. Computation of average velocity includes days of calm, and during the period of record these averaged 24 at North Head, 22 at Newport, and 65 at North Bend. Moreover, none of the three stations here utilized is situated where dune activity is in actual progress, and there can thus be no assurance that the readings obtained are applicable to the desired use. The data furnished by the Weather Bureau are an understatement.

In my field work no systematic collection of velocity data was attempted, but in 1940 and 1941 a few readings, made in connection with other lines of investigation,[4] were obtained on typical days. It has been possible to obtain a record covering the days on which the dune readings were made from unpublished data furnished by the United States Weather Bureau. The dune readings were made on the Coos Bay dune sheet. Those for August 4, 1940, were taken on the beach and adjacent dunes at the north end of Locality 19, the others on the summits of high dune ridges in Localities 20 and 22. The Weather Bureau stations utilized are Newport and North Bend; the dune stations lie between these two points. The Weather Bureau readings were made every 3 hours, with some gaps in the records. A graph, Figure 3, furnishes a comparison between Weather Bureau and dune readings. Velocities at the beach and on the dunes in the daytime are shown to be consistently higher than those at the two stations, in some cases double and even more.

This graph illustrates also the daily wind regime during the summer season: increase in velocity during the forenoon with culmination in the afternoon, followed by decrease to a minimum, sometimes to zero, in the early morning. High afternoon winds are N.-NW. The low-velocity movement at night is for the most part offshore, NE.-SE. winds prevailing. Occasionally N.-NW. winds persist well into the night. No data directly pertinent to the dunes are available for winter. It is certain, however, that the S.-SW. gales are frequently severe, and some attain hurricane violence.

---

[4] The instrument used was a 4-cup anemometer with automatic counter made by Allen E. Chisholm, Portland, Oregon, model 1938, type 2B3C.

At North Head the frequency for winds over 47 m.p.h. was 147 during the period of record—the equivalent of 21 full days in a period of 12½ years. Of these, 128 were S., and the remainder SE-SW.

Since wind data applying directly to the dunes are so scarce, there is justification for introducing as evidence a 1-year record based upon the Beaufort scale taken at

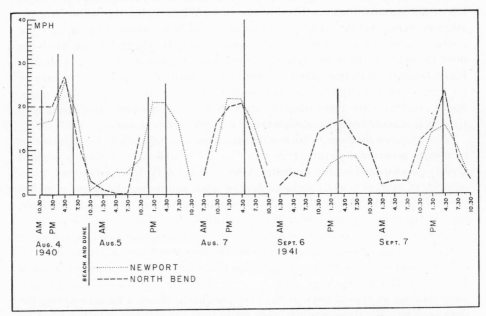

FIGURE 3.—*Wind velocities measured on beach and dunes compared with Weather Bureau measurements for same periods*

the Siuslaw Coast Guard Station in Locality 19 near Florence, Oregon (Table 5). The observations were made from a tower rising above the tree tops 1 km from the shore. Beaufort scale readings are admittedly a rough estimate, and various velocity ranges have been assigned to the scale numbers. The velocity equivalents used here, proposed by C. G. Simpson (Henry, 1926, p. 298), are very conservative. Seventeen occurrences of wind 34 m.p.h. and more were recorded for a single year as against 13 of 32 m.p.h. and more at Newport in 7 years and 22 at North Bend in 6 years.

Factors controlling the wind regime.—Four complex factors constitute the controls: general air circulation, gradients in pressure and temperature between land and sea, cyclonic disturbances, and trend and character of coast.

(1) In summer a permanent high-pressure center lies off the coast at about Long. 150° W., Lat. 40° N. (Schott, 1935). Clockwise movement around this center causes air drift from north to south along the coast of Oregon and Washington. In winter the high-pressure center lies 10° nearer the equator; air drift along the coast, controlled by the Aleutian low, is from south to north.

(2) In summer the temperature of the land (the interior rather than the coastal region) is higher than that of the ocean, and barometric pressure is in general lower.

There is consequently a flow of air from ocean to land. There is a marked diurnal rhythm in this movement, and the maximum is in the afternoon when the gradient is steepest. In winter the temperature and pressure relations are reversed, and air flows from land to ocean. The winter movement is gentle at the coast; at higher levels air passing over the Coast Range must have a higher velocity.

TABLE 5.—*Wind velocity, Beaufort scale, at Siuslaw Coast Guard station, Oregon*
September, 1939 through August, 1940

Beaufort Scale	1	2	3	4	5	6	7	8	9	10
Approx. m.p.h.	0–1	2–3	4–7	8–11	12–16	17–21	22–27	28–33	34–40	41–48
1939 Sept.	..	6	6	7	4	5	1	1	...	...
Oct.	..	11	7	5	4	2	1	...	1	...
Nov.	..	10	8	4	1	5	1	...	1	...
Dec.	..	7	6	4	1	5	1	3	4	...
1940 Jan.	..	7	3	9	5	3	1	2	1	...
Feb.	..	4	3	2	4	3	5	2	4	2
Mar.	..	5	7	4	2	6	4	1	1	1
April	1	3	7	5	8	1	3	1	1	...
May	..	5	3	6	3	5	7	1	1	...
June	1	2	2	6	2	13	4	...	...	...
July	2	7	8	3	2	5	4	...	...	...
Aug.	3	4	4	6	4	6	4	...	...	...
Total	7	71	64	61	40	59	36	11	14	3

(3) Cyclonic disturbances headed eastward pass frequently over the coast. In the latitude of Washington and Oregon they attain maximum frequency and intensity in winter and sink to insignificance in the summer months. They give rise to winds from various directions, but those with highest velocities effective at the shore blow from the south and southwest.

(4) If the onshore winds were controlled only by general air circulation, pressure gradients, and cyclonic disturbances, the resultant movement would be in general southeastward in summer and northeastward in winter. The mountain barrier close to the shore, however, causes deflection of the low-level currents to a direction approaching parallelism to the coastal trend. This effect of the mountain barrier is confirmed by wind behavior at Brookings, near the California line (Lat. 42°). Here the trend of the coast is almost exactly southeastward. The high-velocity winds are again parallel to it: NW. in July, SE. in January.

The prevailing winds north of Cape Blanco are thus in summer confined to the narrow sector N.-NW. with maximum usually at N. The onshore component causes them to attain with remarkable regularity high velocities in the afternoon when the temperature-pressure gradient is steepest. The cyclonic southwest winds of winter strike the coast obliquely and are deflected by the mountain barrier, so that a considerable component part acquires a direction nearly parallel to the coastal trend. This deflection toward parallelism to the coast, occurring both in summer and in winter, is of considerable importance in dune development. The angle at which the wind passes over the beach determines the proportion of sand that finds permanent lodgment: maximum amount when the wind is directly onshore, minimum when it is parallel to the shore. On this coast, where most of the effective surface winds are parallel to the shore or strike it at an acute angle, the amount finding lodgment is close to the minimum.

OCEAN

The ocean as an element in the environment of the dunes is first of all, in its littoral part, the reservoir from which comes the dune sand; the inward and upward surge of water following the break of the waves is the agent that places the sand where it is subject to further transport by the wind. A concomitant relation is transport of sand parallel to the shore which, in conjunction with sources of sand and with barriers of various kinds, determines the relative amounts of subaqueous and beach accumulation at various points along the coast. Littoral drift (sand transport parallel to the shore) is of two sorts: one is "a zigzag longshore transport of bedload debris on the beach slope itself, . . . which is directly traceable to the wave action; and the other, a transport of suspended material by the longshore current, which is an indirect product of the wave action" (Saville, 1950, p. 558). The ultimate cause is wind. Onshore wind from any direction except perpendicular to the shore will bring about coastwise travel of sand.

The wind regime on the coast of Oregon and Washington is such that sand transport is predominantly southward in summer and northward in winter. Twenhofel (1943, p. 24) states that ". . . as the dominant direction of the wind is from the southwest the shore currents move northward for the most part and transport sediment in that direction until headlands prevent." Data given in a previous section indicate that Twenhofel's statement as to prevailing wind direction is far from accurate. The winter winds from south and southwest, it is true, include the strongest of all, but these are relatively infrequent and are not strictly concentrated in direction. The daytime summer winds, on the other hand, though not of exceptional strength, are high in average velocity, relatively constant in occurrence, and largely concentrated in a narrow sector ranging from parallel to the coast to a quadrant offshore, the most effective relation for promoting littoral drift. Furthermore, Saville (1950) obtained data from a model study indicating that, along an infinitely straight beach in equilibrium with a given type of wave, littoral drift is actually greater in volume under the influence of waves of intermediate and low height than is the case with storm waves which erode vigorously but carry most of the material outward to be deposited at greater depths. Absolute equilibrium with a wave type is seldom if ever attained in nature, but if the same type of wave action continues for a long time, as is the case in summer on this coast, equilibrium is approached. Theoretically, then, southward littoral drift characteristic of the summer half of the year should be greater in volume than northward. Evidence based on present movements is inconclusive. Jetties have been built at the mouths of nine rivers and bays on the Washington-Oregon coast. At three of these localities there seems to be accumulation behind the north jetty, indicating predominantly southward drift; two have accumulation behind the south jetty, and four are indefinite.

The relation of dune masses of more than average magnitude to river mouths as partial sources of supply is pertinent to the question. Details are given in Part III; it is sufficient here to state that the evidence seems to indicate predominant northward drift in the north and southward drift in the south. Such dune masses are the cumulative product of millennia of development and may reflect past conditions as well as those of the present. The problem must be left unsolved.

Sand drift in either direction encounters obstacles. At prominent headlands the longshore current is diverted out to sea, and much of the sand in transport is carried beyond the zone of wave influence. Streams with vigorous outflow also probably deflect outward the longshore current. Between any adjoining pair of obstacles there should, therefore, be a seasonal shifting of sand in water transport, back and forth. A certain amount escapes from confinement in both directions; the loss is offset by erosion of the shore and contributions from streams. Because of the many headlands, littoral drift is thus partially localized. If sea level were significantly lower, as has been true in the past, and a continuous coastal plain thus created outside the present headlands, littoral drift would be unhindered except at the mouths of large rivers.

Finally, there is the seasonal cycle in beach processes: erosion by winter storm waves which carry great quantities of sand into deeper water, and rebuilding of the beach by the gentler waves of summer. The character and magnitude of these changes vary greatly in different regions (Shepard, 1948). Precise data for the Oregon coast are not available. It is certain, however, that exceptionally severe winter storms denude certain beaches, attack stabilized dunes, and carry away enormous quantities of sand. In the early days of settlement a lighthouse at the mouth of the Umpqua River was undermined and destroyed (Scott, 1924, p. 48). The destruction wrought at Tillamook Bay and near-by localities will be described in Part III. Such cases of large-scale erosion cannot, however, be attributed to processes of merely seasonal occurrence.

VEGETATION

The dominant vegetation of the coastal strip of Oregon and Washington is a part of the "Pacific Coastal Forest Complex" (Cooper, 1957) which occupies the coastal lowlands and lower mountain slopes from central California to southern Alaska and reaches its maximum development in the Puget Sound region. In size of trees, density, and general luxuriance it is unsurpassed. The principal tree species are western hemlock (*Tsuga heterophylla* (Raf.) Sarg.), western arbor vitae (*Thuja plicata* Donn), and Douglas fir (*Pseudotsuga menziesii* (Mirb.) Franco). Heights of 60 m and more are common. Stands are usually exceedingly dense, and undergrowth and reproduction abundant. One other tree, Port Orford cedar (*Chamaecyparis lawsoniana* (A. Murr.) Parl.), is an important constituent of the Coast Range forest from the California line to a point a few km north of Coos Bay.

The trees named above all reach the vicinity of the ocean shore, but in the immediate coastal strip two other species are of great importance: Sitka spruce (*Picea sitchensis* (Bong.) Carr.) and lodgepole pine (*Pinus contorta* Dougl.). Sitka spruce is the coastal tree *par excellence*. It forms extensive forests, continuous for long distances, on the terraces, the seaward-facing mountain slopes, and exposed headlands, and attains its largest size on alluvial deposits at the heads of bays. In pure stands many trees are uniformly 60 m in height and 1–2 m in diameter. Such stands are even-aged and youthful—sometimes only a century and a half old. Uniform reproduction after blowdown by severe winter storms seems to be the explanation of this condition. Lodgepole pine is a comparatively small and short-lived tree; it attains a height of 30 m and an age of not much more than a century. Like Sitka spruce it is resistant to the desiccating effects of the ocean wind and to the sand and salt spray borne by it, and occupies equally exposed situations, where individuals of both species and even whole stands are often strikingly streamlined. The special importance of the pine lies in its rapid occupation of burned-over areas. Ring counts in even-aged stands furnish approximate dates for recent fires.

Trees, singly and in forest growth, and certain lower plants as well, are factors in dune development that cannot be ignored. Discussion of the various roles they play as geological agents is reserved until the interaction of the three purely physical components of the system—sand, wind, and water—have been considered. One very general effect may be stated here. A forest of the character described above, extraordinary in height and density, presents an extremely effective obstacle to the advance of sand toward the interior. The belt of dunes is thus restricted, but because of the slowness of forward movement the sand piles up into masses of unusual height.

HUMAN OCCUPANCE
MAN'S INFLUENCE IN GENERAL

Coastal dunes in many parts of the world have been modified by the activities of man. This is particularly true of western Europe, where the coastal areas have been thickly populated for many centuries. The effects are seen both in acceleration of activity or complete rejuvenation and in attempts at control where dunes threaten damage or destruction.

Rejuvenation, partial or complete, has been due principally to grazing, cutting of trees for timber and shrubs for fuel, collection of dune grasses for thatch, and in one case at least to burrowing of rabbits maintained for game—followed by digging out of the self-same rodents when they became too numerous. Van Dieren (1934), in his study of the dunes of the island Terschelling on the Netherlands coast, states (p. 174) that "... without a doubt these human and biotic influences down through the centuries have been the most important factor leading to eolian redisposition. Had it not been for human beings, the dune region would present an entirely different appearance today." Solger (1910) states that the dunes of the Kurische Nehrung on the coast of East Prussia were deforested by the Russians during the Seven Years War (1756–1763) and have been active ever since. According to Cockayne (1911, p. 17–18), grazing instituted by the early settlers of New Zealand, with burning as a supposed means of improving the range, resulted in conversion of extensive areas of thoroughly stabilized dunes into seas of moving sand. In North

America on Cape Cod widespread rejuvenation occurred owing to destruction of forest and to pasturage (Westgate, 1904, p. 18).

For centuries systematic attempts have been made to control the movement of dunes when it became a menace to human activity, for the most part by planting marram grass (*Ammophila arenaria* (L.) Link)—and again mainly in western Europe. The most outstanding example is the tremendous project in the great dune region of Les Landes on the coast of the Bay of Biscay, initiated by Brémontier in 1787 and completed in 1864. A broad strip of coastal dunes was converted into a productive forest of pine (Harlé and Harlé, 1920; and other authors).

It is obvious that no treatment of the dune environment is complete without appraisal of man as an essential element in it. For Oregon and Washington two periods must be recognized: prehistoric time, during which the coast was sparsely populated by paleo-Indians and Indians, and the brief period since the arrival of the European whites.

PREHISTORIC PERIOD

Research indicates more and more definitely that man has been present in the Pacific regions of North America for thousands of years. For example, hearths and artifacts have been found east of the Cascades in association with bones of extinct animals both above and below the Mt. Mazama ash layer (Cressman, 1946). Since a coastal region is in many ways superior to an interior area for human occupance, a contemporary population on the coast may be assumed.

The Oregon coast abounds in relics of occupation by Indians of relatively recent time—kitchen middens, dwellings, and graves (Chase, 1873; Schumacher, 1874; 1877). In my exploration of the Coos Bay dune sheet, five occupation sites were discovered within its limits. All had small rounded cobbles, discolored and broken by heat; charcoal, bones, and shells were found at most, and at one a mano or pounding stone. Two sites were located close to the mouth of the Siuslaw River in Locality 20; they rested on a well-developed podzolized soil layer and were covered by a few meters of dune sand, which in one case bore forest. Two others in Locality 22 were much more deeply buried; remnants of dune masses that once covered them bore trees up to 286 years old. It is thus evident that the dunes were visited by the aboriginal inhabitants for at least several centuries before the present, and that the aborigines built fires upon them which sometimes spread out of control; fire has been an important factor in dune processes as far back as we can trace them.

HISTORIC PERIOD

The historic period on the Washington-Oregon coast technically begins with the early navigators, but the first attempt to establish settlement on the coast—at the mouth of the Umpqua River—was not made until 1850. In 1852 gold was discovered in the black sands of the beaches (Bancroft, 1888, vol. 2, p. 329). During the 1850's both coal and timber (especially Port Orford cedar) began to be shipped to San Francisco (Scott, 1924, p. 51–52).

During the past hundred years the lumber industry has removed vast amounts of forest growth in coastal Oregon and Washington, and fires have wrought havoc there. The forests on the dunes themselves, however, have been affected little by either agent of destruction during the historic period, because most of the present trees are of inferior quality, and the coastal situation and frequent discontinuity of the forest expose them to a minimum of danger from fire originating outside their own limits. Cattle have grazed within the boundaries of the Coos Bay dune sheet for at least 60 years (Emil Peterson, personal communication). For the most part they have kept to low ground where feed was abundant, moving to higher areas when the depressions were flooded. Rejuvenation from this cause has occurred on a considerable scale between Coos Bay and Tenmile Creek where suitable lands for grazing are most extensive. The effects, however, are confined for the most part to the low portions of the dune complex; the main topographic features have not been changed significantly. Cranberry culture is carried on in certain areas; its effects are local and insignificant. In summary, the influence of man in causing renewal of dune activity has not been great, except for his responsibility in the starting of fires during prehistoric times.

Control of dune activity on the coasts of North America is not nearly so pressing a problem as on European coasts, where every bit of land must be protected for utilization, and yet in many places local measures of control have been found necessary. On the coast of Oregon moving dunes are a threat to highways and to railroads and are constantly dumping sand into certain river-mouth harbors. Early efforts at control were individual and haphazard. In recent years several co-operating federal agencies have initiated a large-scale dune-control project based upon careful study of the scientific principles involved. Establishment of marram grass is considered merely as the first step in the process. It is followed by planting of other grasses and herbs, then of shrubs, and finally trees, both native and introduced. This sequence parallels the natural vegetation succession upon dunes. In practice as in nature, establishment of forest is the ultimate goal (Kellogg, 1915; Rowalt, 1936; Steele, 1940; Arnst, 1942a; 1942b; McLaughlin and Brown, 1942).

A very recent effect of man upon the dunes is an attempt to develop them as a source of water for industrial purposes. Experimental operations in Locality 23, just north of Coos Bay, indicate that the dune sand is in communication with an aquifer originating in the Coast Range and that a considerable flow of water may be obtained from it. If the operation is successful and long-continued, effects upon water table and vegetation, and thus upon mobility of the sand, may follow.

PART II: DUNE FORMS AND PROCESSES

INTRODUCTION

The simplest possible combination of elements in the field of dune phenomena comprises sand and wind and results in a pattern characterized by repetition of almost identical forms. When water is added as a third element, the forms are altered somewhat, but uniformity persists. Uniformity prevails in these two cases because the influence of the factors upon the sand mass is uniform or varies rhythmically. A fourth element, vegetation, introduces diversity and irregularity; there are, however, certain forms that are characteristic of this combination.

The sand-wind system is confined to deserts, but even here the water factor may not be completely ignored. On some desert coasts where dunes occur—notably that of Peru-Chile—plants are of no consequence, but in most regions of coastal dunes they are of great importance. This does not imply, however, the absence on coasts of situations where sand, wind, and water are the only components of the system. On the coast of Oregon, for example, there are extensive areas of dunes devoid of plants, and the resulting forms are closely related to those of arid regions, even deserts.

Where sand, wind, and water are concerned, pattern is a more useful concept than the individual "dune". On the Oregon coast there are two such patterns. One is close-textured, made up of ridges transverse to the wind, the units being comparatively small in scale. The transverse-ridge pattern has been many times described, but there is still much to be said concerning it. The other, made up of massive, widely spaced units, I have called the "oblique-ridge pattern." Nothing exactly corresponding to it has been discovered in the literature. Its constituent units seem closest to the rather controversial "longitudinal dunes" of various arid regions. Aufrère (1935, p. 482) distinguished "major" and "minor" forms in the Algerian Sahara. The same distinction may be made here. The oblique ridges, the major forms, are determined by the complete wind regime; the transverse ridges, the minor forms, by the summer winds alone.

After a brief section dealing with the nature and sources of the dune sand, the two patterns will be considered as they occur on the coast of Oregon. Discussion of the system sand-wind-water-vegetation will follow.

NATURE AND SOURCES OF THE DUNE SAND

Twenhofel (1943; 1946) has made a comprehensive study of the sands of the Oregon beaches in which some attention is given to the sands of the dunes. Present discussion is based largely on facts and figures provided by these two reports. Table 6, abridged from Twenhofel's Table 12 (1946), gives representative analyses, mechanical and mineral, of dune-sand samples collected along the coast between Coos Bay and the Columbia River. Mechanical analysis demonstrates the extremely narrow range in size of particles. In eight of the nine samples the proportion by weight of particles between an eighth and half a mm ranged from 97.9 per cent to 100 per cent. This concentration is characteristic of dune sand in general. In coastal dunes, it may be

25

noted, a considerable part of the sorting has been done by water before wind takes hold.

Mineralogically, the sand particles are for the most part quartz and feldspar. Twenhofel did not separate these, but quartz is without doubt predominant. The

TABLE 6.—*Mechanical and mineral analyses of sands from Oregon coastal dunes*
Abridged from Twenhofel, 1946, Table 12

	Mechanical				Mineral			
	1–½ mm	½–¼ mm	¼–⅛ mm	⅛–1/16 mm	Quartz Feldspar	Olivine Epidote Garnet	Magnetite Ilmenite Chromite	Rock*
1. Coos Bay Spit, Coast Guard trail to beach	..	56.30	43.40	0.30	85.25	...	trace	14.75
2. Coos Bay Spit, 9 miles north of Coast Guard trail.	..	33.10	66.40	0.50	83.95	...	trace	16.05
3. One mile south of Saunders Lake Coast Guard trail: dune above beach	..	77.50	22.50	trace	79.40	...	trace	20.60
4. Saunders Lake Coast Guard trail: 1 mile from sea	..	48.70	50.50	0.80	93.40	0.30	0.40	5.90
5. Middle of Umpqua Spit, about 1 mile north of river mouth	0.40	39.60	59.55	0.45	97.30	0.05	0.20	2.45
6. South of Tahkenitch Creek, about 1 mile from sea	0.60	50.90	47.00	1.50	94.60	trace	trace	5.40
7. Sand Lake, a fourth to half a mile from sea	..	50.00	48.90	1.10	90.55	0.30	0.60	8.55
8. Three miles north of Neskowin Creek	..	66.50	33.00	0.50	81.00	2.20	0.35	16.45
9. Sunset Beach Road: present foredune	..	7.90	86.40	5.70	70.80	trace	1.10	28.10

* Miscellaneous particles of mixed or uncertain composition.

quartz and feldspar particles are commonly subangular to well rounded and have a shining surface. Particles of the heavy minerals are scarce, as they were left behind with the beach sand where locally they have accumulated in considerable quantities and give rise to the "black sands," which in early days were worked extensively for gold and platinum, and recently because of fairly abundant chromite.

The ultimate source of the dune-sand particles may be as far away as the Rocky Mountains of Canada, but the immediate sources are principally two: erosion of formations exposed to wave attack, and outflow from rivers. It is perhaps impossible to determine which is the more important over the coast as a whole. Tertiary formations border the Oregon coast, and these are for the most part sediments with a large proportion of sandstone, which succumbs readily to wave attack. Considerable amounts are derived from the unconsolidated terrace beds, and the dunes themselves suffer erosion. The relative amounts of sediment supplied by various rivers are indicated very roughly by their average water discharge. For the Columbia this is

195,000 cubic feet per second (U. S. Geol. Survey, 1954). All the others are insignificant in comparison. Discharge for the Umpqua, largest river between the Columbia and Cape Blanco, is 7177 cfs. For the Nehalem and Alsea, with drainage areas entirely within the Coast Range, the figures are 2630 and 1455 cfs respectively. The largest rivers supply sediment faster than the longshore currents can move it along the coast. Much of it therefore goes ashore before it travels far, and the dunes adjacent to these river mouths are correspondingly massive. The Columbia is of course an outstanding example; it is conspicuously true also of the Umpqua and the Siuslaw.

SAND, WIND, AND WATER: THE TRANSVERSE-RIDGE PATTERN
VALIDITY OF THE CONCEPT

Systems of parallel transverse ridges occur the world over wherever wind constant in direction has to deal with heavy accumulations of sand unencumbered with vegetation.[5] The existence of such systems would seem to be a fact verifiable by simple observation. At least two authors, however, have asserted the contrary.

Enquist (1932, p. 26) stressed " . . . the fact that so-called transverse dunes, or dunes at right angles with the wind-direction, are never formed, or at least, not maintained in regions devoid of vegetation."

Bagnold, usually carefully inductive in method, asserts (1941, p. 205) that " . . . dunes, though they may be isolated or longitudinal, are never transverse to the wind". He reasons as follows (p. 206): "If a small chance lowering occurs in the crest line of a long transverse dune, the local increase of wind velocity through the gap causes a rise in the rate of sand movement there, with a consequent removal of sand from the surface of the gap. The gap gets bigger, and a *blow-out* is formed."

The blow-out mass moves forward faster than the remaining parts of the ridge and becomes separated from them. "A dune has, in fact, been born . . . . The same instability must occur at other places along the ridge. Consequently the ridge must break up into a number of isolated dunes" (p. 207). These are barchans. Cholnoky (1902) had much earlier expressed a somewhat similar view: that the transverse ridge, whereas it does actually occur, is an unstable and transitional form.

Bagnold's viewpoint may perhaps be traced to the fact that in the deserts of northeast Africa the dunes are sand masses usually definitely circumscribed and resting on a hard substratum. Where the substratum is incompletely covered there is an undoubted tendency toward formation of barchans. Melton, in a study of the dunes of the southern High Plains of North America (1940, p. 119), states that isolated transverse ridges " . . . do not endure long even under the most constant conditions. With slight irregularities in wind direction, or in the resistance of the sandy soil, they go to pieces in a few days or weeks yielding isolated sand hills of the 'barcan' type." It seems clear that isolated transverse ridges of some length do occur on a hard substratum but are unstable.

---

[5] North African deserts: Rolland (1881), Cornish (1897; 1900; 1914); Turkestan: Hedin (1904); west coast of France: Harlé and Harlé (1920); plains and deserts of Western United States: Melton (1940), H. T. U. Smith (1940), Hack (1941), and others. The type occurs also on the coasts of southern California and Baja California. It has been described in works of general scope by Sokolow (1894), Free (1911), and Högbom (1923).

The barchan itself, however, is fundamentally a transverse ridge. An extended transverse ridge completely isolated on a hard substratum has at its ends leeward-projecting tails like those of the barchan. The barchan is merely a transverse ridge laterally compressed until it is approximately isodiametric. It does not merit the position of importance that has been given it in dune studies; it is a variation possessing striking individuality and great beauty that develops under particular conditions. Setting it up as the "fundamental" or "ideal" unit of dune morphology, or as one of several (Cholnoky, 1902; Hedin, 1904, vol. 1, p. 351; Walther, 1924, p. 125; von Engeln and Caster, 1952, p. 298) is not justified. Discussion as to whether the transverse ridge is actually or theoretically composed of fused barchans seems equally pointless. The fact that certain segments of the transverse ridge often acquire "barchanoid" form is capable of simple and direct explanation without appeal to evolutional history. It is due simply to the action of air currents which converge at the inevitable low places in the crest and fan out beyond. The result is a concave slipface beneath each summit.

Aside from all dunes isolated on a hard substratum, there are the surface forms developed on deep continuous sand, and these are just as worthy of the name of "dunes" as are the others. Among such, the transverse ridge is a perfectly distinct entity and is stable in that it maintains its individuality as it moves forward. Figure 3 of Plate 7 and descriptions by many authors, including some from the Sahara (Rolland, 1881; Aufrère, 1931; 1933; 1935; Bourcart, 1938) are flatly contradictory to Bagnold's sweeping statement. It is particularly interesting to find an aerial photograph depicting a well-developed system of anastomosing transverse ridges on the back of a huge barchan in Peru (Rich, 1942, Fig. 274).

OCCURRENCE ON THE OREGON-WASHINGTON COAST

The transverse-ridge pattern occurs in nearly all the major dune localities on the Oregon coast, reaching its finest development on the Coos Bay dune sheet. It is of little importance on the Washington coast, as there are few sufficient expanses of open sand there. It occupies a strip adjoining the beach or separated from it by a rudimentary foredune. Inland it merges with the oblique-ridge pattern where that is present. Transverse ridges climb up and over the seaward ends of the oblique ridges, and the corridors between the latter are often invaded by them. The pattern is seen at its best in Locality 20, where it covers the spit south of the Siuslaw River (Pl. 7, fig. 3) and extends without a break 16 km to the mouth of Siltcoos River and beyond, attaining its greatest width opposite Woahink Lake (Pl. 7, fig. 1). Other conspicous areas are at the extreme north end of the dune sheet in Locality 19 (Pl. 7, fig. 2) and on the spit north of the Umpqua River. The interior areas of bare sand in Locality 19, surrounded by forested dunes, are for the most part characterized by this pattern.

FORM, STRUCTURE, AND SIZE OF RIDGES

The following description applies to the Oregon coast under conditions of summer, during which the pattern attains perfection of development. The seasonal cycle will be treated in a later section.

The ridges vary greatly in length, are rather indeterminate, and frequently anastomose. In some places along a crest is what seems to be its termination in an area without obvious plan. It is evident from Figure 1 of Plate 7, however, that such an appearance may be deceptive; in spite of apparent breaks, crests may be traced from the air for long distances, sometimes for a kilometer or more. In detail they are somewhat sinuous. The crests are far from uniform in elevation; they show a succession of arching summits with cols between (Pl. 8, fig. 1).

The windward slopes of the ridges are long and gentle; various authors give figures from similar dunes ranging from 3° to 12°. The lee slopes are characterized by a slipface,[6] the steepest possible for sliding sand, averaging about 33°. Along most of the ridge the slipface occupies only a portion of the lee slope; above it, extending backward from its sharply defined upper edge, is a gently convex surface which meets the windward slope at the rounded summit. Opposite the high points of the ridge the slipface is horizontally concave to leeward and in some places extends upward to the actual crest, which is thus relatively sharp (Pl. 8, fig. 1). It is lowest, and convex to leeward, opposite the cols. Individual slipface units vary in length from the extent of a single concavity beneath a high point to hundreds of meters, including a number of bulges and re-entrants. In places the slipface is absent, and the lee slope is gentle from top to bottom.

The internal structure of the ridge is characterized by a complicated system of cross-bedding, described by Lahee (1923, p. 82–84), Thompson (1937, p. 748–749), and Twenhofel (1950, p. 344). Foresets, due to sedimentation on the slipface, make the bulk of the mass; topsets, from deposition on the windward slope, also occur. The dip of the foresets is of course to leeward, but its exact direction varies greatly owing for the most part to the sinuous trend of the slipface. The dip of the topsets is to windward, is gentle, and probably more uniform in direction than the foresets.

The structure is plainly shown on surfaces where a portion of the moist dune mass has been planed away by the wind. The truncated foresets appear as concentric arcs which may be concave either to windward or to leeward; and such structure is apparent in the lowest depressions among the ridges, even within 1–2 m of sea level.

Casual observation seems to show that the transverse ridges are smallest near the shore and largest at the inner edge of the bare sand. An attempt was made to discover by measurements upon aerial photographs whether this impression is correct.

As a measure of size of ridge, distance between crests is the only available dimension. Since geometric form is essentially constant, intercrest distance is a fair measure of magnitude of the ridge. Because of sinuosity of the crests, considerable irregularity in intercrest distance is to be expected along any given line. This situation was met by dividing total distance along a line into units of 200 m and averaging intercrest distances for each unit. The lines were drawn perpendicular to the average of ridge trends upon a tracing of the photographs in which only the crests were indicated. Three sets of measurements were made, all in Locality 20.

In the area opposite Woahink Lake the line extended from the shore southeastward a distance of 3000 m. The number of ridges included was 82. It is evident from Figure 4 that intercrest distance, and therefore size of ridges, increases inland but not regularly; groups of larger ridges alternate with groups of smaller ones.

---

[6] This excellent term was introduced by Bagnold (1941). Other terms that have been used are "sandfall", "Steildüne", "talus", "l'à pic d'envahissement."

A second set of measurements was made 6.5 km north of the first, opposite the village of Glenada (Fig. 4B). The line measured was 1800 m long, and the number of ridges was 55. Increase in intercrest distance is here more regular. A third set was

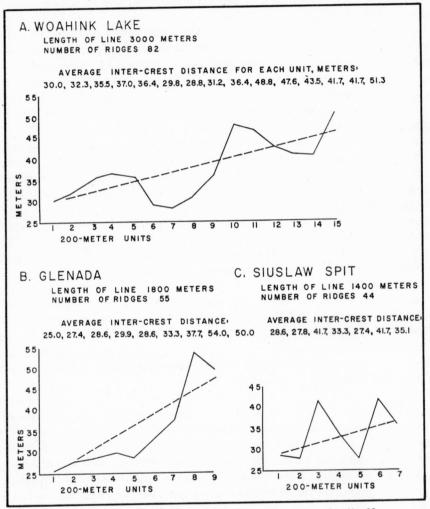

FIGURE 4.—*Intercrest distances on transverse-ridge pattern, Locality 20* Along three lines.

made 2.5 km north of the second on the broad spit at the mouth of the Siuslaw River (Fig. 4C). There were 44 ridges in a distance of 1400 m. Intercrest distance is irregular, but a slight general increase inland is apparent. It thus appears that the ridges do increase in size inland but not regularly.

Where transverse ridges occur inland of the main strip dominated by the pattern they are definitely larger—for example, where they climb upon the outer ends of the oblique ridges, in the valleys between the latter, and particularly in the interior areas of bare sand in Locality 19.

There is a secondary but prominent and characteristic feature of the pattern which, for want of a better term, I call the "lee-projection." It is a tongue of sand extending to leeward from the slipface and apparently attached to it, almost always directly beneath a high point on the ridge crest (Pl. 8, fig. 3). Its juncture with the slipface is sharply marked, but it merges insensibly with the windward slope of the next ridge. The crest is a very gentle arc concave to the east.

An interesting feature, strikingly apparent from the air (Pl. 7, fig. 1), but not easily realized on the ground, is the strong tendency of lee-projections related to successive ridges to arrange themselves in long lines trending with the wind. Some of these may be traced for a kilometer or more, and they are so numerous as to produce in combination with the transverse ridges a reticulate pattern with rhomboidal meshes. Since the lee-projections are attached at the high points of the ridges it follows that the latter are also in line; the same must be true for the intervening cols.

TREND OF RIDGES IN RELATION TO WIND DIRECTION

For detailed study three single vertical photographs were selected which depict widely separated areas along the coast. The first is at the extreme north end of the dune sheet opposite Lily Lake, Locality 19. The second is 20 km south, opposite the south end of Woahink Lake, Locality 20. The third is 34 km farther, opposite Eel Lake, Locality 22. The photographs were made September 21, 1940; they show the final result of one complete season of dominant north-northwesterly wind.

Certain features of the dunes are reasonably accurate indicators of average direction of summer wind at the earth's surface. Most dependable are the "tongue hills" immediately adjoining the beach. These are slender deposits lying in the lee of clumps of marram grass and logs and stumps and tapering to a point downwind. As they are fixed only at the windward end they are free to shift with changing wind, but their straightness and the considerable length of many indicate that fluctuation is unimportant. A shifting wind will turn the extreme tip, but the trend of the main body is only slightly affected. Wind direction thus indicated applies to the season in which the measurements were made, but the average of 10 measurements of trend made in the same part of Locality 20 on aerophotos taken after an interval of 13 years is identical with that derived from the first set. Incidentally, tongue hills were fewer and much less distinct in 1953 than in 1940 because of increased density of marram grass.

Trends of the tongue hills and other features were determined as follows. For each photograph a north-south line was established by matching the coast line on the picture with the same location on the topographic map. Using tracing film superposed upon the photograph, trends of a number of tongues were drawn, the angles with the north-south line measured, and the average taken. The results are shown graphically in Figure 5.

At Lily Lake the average trend of 10 tongue hills was S. 17.5°E., of 10 at Woahink Lake S. 11°E., and of 5 at Eel Lake S. 1.5°E. (Fig. 5A).[7] The surface wind current at the beach thus travels in a direction a few degrees east of south, and as one goes southward it moves progressively closer to the north-south line and also closer to the trend of the coast.

---

[7] Close correspondence of trends in a given locality made a large number of determinations unnecessary.

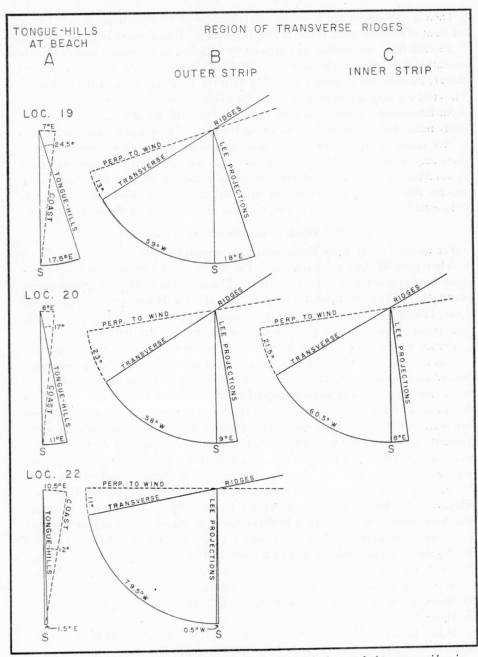

FIGURE 5.—*Average trends of tongue hills at the beach, of lee-projections, and of transverse ridges in relation to summer wind direction and trend of coast*
Localities 19, 20, 22

The next step was to plot trends of lee projections in a strip adjoining the beach 650 m wide. Fifteen were used at Lily Lake, and 40 each at Woahink Lake and Eel Lake (Fig. 5B). Agreement among these is naturally not so close as in the case of the tongue hills, since irregularities of topography cause unpredictable deflections of surface currents. The average in each locality, however, agrees closely with that of the corresponding group of tongue hills, and the shift toward the north-south line southward is naturally also about the same. Thus the lee projections may also be taken as indices of surface wind direction.

Finally, trends of transverse ridges were determined for this strip in the same way; 12 were used at Lily Lake, and 40 each at Woahink Lake and Eel Lake. Agreement here is still less close, since on account of sinuosity of the ridges their straight-line trends could be merely approximated.

At the Woahink Lake locality, where the zone is broadest, trends of ridges and lee projections were determined in a second strip east of the first and of the same width (Fig. 5C). It is evident that relations are uniform throughout the area.

In the literature it is commonly stated that the trend of transverse dune ridges is perpendicular to the direction of the controlling wind. For the Oregon coast this seems not to be strictly true. The lee-projections align themselves with the wind; the transverse ridges deviate from the perpendicular to it. Deviation is everywhere the same in kind: the angle to leeward of the ridge between it and lee-projection opening seaward is always the lesser. Aerophotos made in 1953 show the same angular relation between ridge and lee-projection. The reason for this deviation has not been discovered.

WAVE FORM

The surface of a dune sheet upon which the transverse-ridge pattern is well developed suggests almost irresistibly a water surface ruffled into waves by the wind. Certain authors have maintained that such ridges are true waves, some of them by implication or with reservations (Baschin, 1899, p. 420; Hedin, 1904, vol. 2, p. 412; Cornish, 1914, p. 52, and earlier publications; Exner, 1920; 1921; 1927). Others assert that a dune ridge is not a true wave and point out certain characteristics which they consider to be decisively against such an interpretation (Cholnoky, 1902, p. 106; Högbom, 1923).

The controversy seems based on confusion of ideas, since the term "wave" has been applied to a heterogeneous assemblage of phenomena which resemble each other only in rhythmic transmission of energy. The case being discussed is within an extensive category of phenomena, superficially alike, in which the common feature is development of a sinusoidal surface of discontinuity between two adjacent media. As widely differing examples the following are offered: the surface of discontinuity in the atmosphere made manifest by "mackerel sky"; the large-scale "polar front", which is a "surface of discontinuity between the mild westerly currents of middle latitudes and the cold currents of high latitudes" (Brunt, 1939, p. 318); water waves; current ripples in sand under water; eolian sand ripples; transverse dune ridges (disregarding the slipface, a special feature); the vortex sheet which trails to leeward from the top of a dune; ripples and ridges in snow. In all these the two adjacent media differ in relative velocity. Where both media are fluids the plane surface of discontinuity tends to be re-established soon after relative velocity becomes zero; where a solid phase is concerned it retains its wavelike form.

The classic pronouncement by Helmholtz, pertaining to fluids only, has often been cited as an explanation of the regular wave form of dunes. Helmholtz stated (1889, p. 767, 778–9) that, when two fluids differing in relative velocity are in contact, a large number of the possible stationary wave motions require a smaller supply of energy than does the corresponding flow with a plane surface of discontinuity. It follows from this, he says, that the system in the case of a plane surface, as against such wave motions, is in a state of unstable equilibrium. The sinusoidal surface expresses a sort of dynamic but stable equilibrium.

Applied to fluids alone, as Helmholtz intended, this seems another way of stating the facts rather than a basic explanation. Transference to a system including a solid phase, unsupported by experiment or theory, smacks of unjustifiable analogy.

The crucial point is the impulse which produces initial distortion of a theoretical plane surface of discontinuity. I suggest that in the cases cited above a local oblique impact of a component of one phase of the system upon the other provides this impulse. Where one of the phases is a fluid and the other a solid, the impact is delivered by the former. An irregularity in the surface of the latter, although not essential, will intensify the effects of turbulence.

The points of impact are numerous and irregularly distributed. Irregularity passes into regularity. The mechanics of the transition are obscure, but two constituent processes which go on simultaneously are distinguishable. In profiles parallel to the wind the sinuosities become approximately uniform in size and spacing; the sinuosities of neighboring profiles tend to fall into step. Joining of crests and of troughs in lines transverse to wind direction is thus attained. A clear-cut presentation of the facts seems to be all that one may at present attempt.

Theoretical development of the wave pattern from a plane surface of discontinuity is oversimplified when applied to any extensive area of transverse ridges. The Coos Bay dune sheet is the product of centuries of varied history; any attempt to trace its complete ontogeny is hopeless. Each winter the transverse ridges are partially obliterated. Each summer they are again brought to perfection. The pattern changes in detail from year to year but not in general character nor perceptibly in scale. To all appearances it is in equilibrium with its present environment.

A system of transverse ridges will develop under the following conditions: (1) unidirectional general air flow parallel to a land surface smooth and free from significant obstacles; (2) an atmospheric state permitting the surficial sand to dry out and remain dry for weeks or months; (3) depth of sand sufficient to prevent exposure of the substratum in the interridge troughs; (4) a supply of new material sufficient to maintain the last-named state. On the coast of Oregon conditions as to sand are met in the littoral strip and some other places; wind and atmosphere are favorable in the summer months.

PROFILE OF THE INDIVIDUAL RIDGE

Importance of aerodynamic theory.—The characteristic profile of a mature transverse ridge is asymmetric, with a gentle slope to windward, variable in inclination, and a steep face with fixed inclination occupying part or all of the leeward slope. This profile is maintained essentially unchanged as the ridge progresses. Hundreds of pages have been devoted to attempted explanation of the phenomena involved, but these have been for the most part unsatisfactory, partly because adequate knowledge of basic aerodynamic principles has not been available, and in some cases because conclusions have been founded on false premises. Lack of basic knowledge has recently been greatly reduced through rapid development of the science of aerodynamics.[8]

Two authors have drawn upon this source. Dobrowolski (1924) gave a very detailed theoretical treatment of the behavior of air currents in contact with obstacles of various geometric shapes. His application of principles to the special problems of dunes was, however, unsatisfactory. The work of Bagnold (1935; 1937; 1941) is a rigidly mathematical treatment based mainly on experiment. My own nonmathematical exposition, founded upon aerodynamical theory,[9] had been almost completed before Bagnold's comprehensive publication appeared. Though differing somewhat in approach, there is no essential conflict between his (1941, p. 195–205) and mine, except with regard to stability or instability of the transverse ridge. Bagnold (1941, p. 205–207) is dealing with the individual isolated ridge; my view is that the pattern is more significant than the constituent units.

Bagnold does not consider the case of a fluid in contact with a smooth surface, as sandy surfaces are rough. But, since some readers may be unfamiliar with the field, it seems desirable to begin with the simplest case. Modifications due to roughness will be noted, and finally consideration will be given to actual conditions pertaining to dune surfaces where sand grains may be dislodged and transported by the air current. Since only the profile of the ridge is concerned, discussion will be confined to two-dimensional flow.

Air flow related to the surface of a solid.—When air flows over a perfectly smooth surface, an exceedingly thin layer lying next to it adheres, and therefore has zero relative velocity. Next to it is a stratum characterized by a velocity gradient from zero to speed of the general flow; this is the boundary layer. At first the flow within it is laminar; *i.e.*, each successive layer slides over the one beneath it with speed increasing with distance from the surface. With sufficient length of travel along the surface transition occurs; the flow becomes turbulent.

At this point it is necessary to introduce a nondimensional quantity, Reynolds number, which determines the configuration of flow related to geometrically similar objects. The symbols used vary with different authors; Dommasch (1953) gives the equation as $R_N = \dfrac{VL}{\nu}$, where V is the velocity of the general flow of the fluid, L some

---

[8] Strahler (1952, p. 927–928) has emphasized the importance of fluid dynamics to the geomorphologist: "The work of running water, waves, and wind cannot be understood without a thorough appreciation of the principles of laminar and turbulent flow. Fluid dynamics is, therefore, a cornerstone of geomorphology".

[9] The works consulted are as follows: Prandtl (1927), Dryden *et al.* (1932), Dodge and Thompson (1937), Piercy (1937), Goldstein *et al.* (1938), Dryden (1941), Haurwitz (1941), Jones (1942), Liepmann and Puckett (1947), Milne-Thomson (1948), Streeter (1948), Binder (1949), Dwinnell (1949), Kuethe and Schetzer (1950), Dommasch (1953), von Kármán (1954), and a number of special contributions.

convenient linear dimension of the object, and v the kinematic viscosity[10] of the fluid. Assuming similar geometric forms (and with certain qualifications), if the Reynolds numbers are the same, the configurations of flow will be the same. In the present discussion one fluid—air—is concerned; therefore v is almost constant and may be ignored. Behavior of the flow thus depends on velocity of the fluid and a dimension of the object.

For the following theoretical discussion it will be convenient to assume as the object a protuberance from a plane, whose surface profile is the arc of a circle similar to that of a low incipient dune. Height of the protuberance above the plane is taken as L, and this for the present is kept constant; therefore V is left as the only variable, and the value of R_N depends wholly on it.

With general air flow of sufficiently low velocity (low Reynolds number); the boundary layer remains in contact with the surface throughout almost the entire length of the protuberance—a condition known as streamlining.

With increase in general velocity, there is on the lee side of the protuberance increase in pressure. Flow in the boundary layer is thus opposed by an adverse pressure gradient. With sufficient increase in general velocity, the flow within the boundary layer very close to the surface, with least velocity, will no longer be able to make headway; forward motion will cease, and a small reverse movement will follow. The boundary layer is forced away from the surface and becomes a free layer; separation has taken place. With only moderate increase in general velocity, the free layer rolls up into a stationary vortex; it remains attached. With further increase in general velocity, the forces due to inertia dominate over those due to viscosity, and the free layer moves off downwind, bounded above by the main flow and below by stagnant air. It seems invariably to take a sinusoidal form in accordance with the general principle discussed in the preceding section. There is always a tendency, in addition, to roll up at intervals, which produces major vortices that travel downwind in regular procession until they finally disintegrate. The rolling-up tendency is to be traced to the vertical velocity gradient in the boundary layer, developed while still in contact with the surface.

Assuming velocity just sufficient to cause separation, if height L of the protuberance is increased without changing the radius of curvature, i.e., geometric form remaining the same, velocity V must be decreased to maintain R_N constant. Accordingly the critical velocity for separation will be lowered.

If radius of curvature is decreased while height of the protuberance is kept the same, the geometric shape is changed—it becomes more convex, the curvature is more abrupt. The current threads on the lee side spread more abruptly, and the pressure gradient which the boundary layer must encounter becomes steeper. With general velocity unchanged, separation will occur sooner, i.e., closer to the apex of the protuberance. If the curve is broken abruptly, ahead of the point where separation would normally take place under existing conditions of V and L, forming an

---

[10] "The coefficient of kinematic viscosity (v) is the ratio of the coefficient of viscosity (μ) to the density" (Jones, 1942, p. 10); i.e., $v = \dfrac{\mu}{\rho}$

edge, the radius of curvature at the edge is zero, and separation will take place at that point.

Turbulence within the boundary layer has a modifying effect. The boundary layer and the free layer are thicker because there is molar interchange of momentum in addition to molecular. Because of the velocity gradient in the boundary layer, turbulence takes on a special character: it is affected with vorticity. The free layer may be termed the vortex layer.

The surface has so far been assumed to be smooth. Roughness introduces further modifications. Turbulence in the boundary layer is increased, and the layer itself may be many times thicker.

Air flow over a body of loose sand.—Bagnold (1941) has given us a very satisfactory picture of the mechanics of dislodgment and transport of sand grains. Initial dislodgment is of course due to direct wind pressure. There are three types of transport: suspension, saltation, and surface creep.

Most sand grains are too large to be carried in true suspension, but upward currents may check the descent of a grain and cause it to travel a considerable distance through the air (Bagnold, 1941, p. 37).

In saltation the grains "move like ping-pong balls," and strike the surface at a low angle; if the grains themselves are not dislodged, the grains doing the striking rebound into the air for a second leap (Bagnold, 1941, p. 19). If the sand bed contains many grains of comparatively large size, rebound of the bombarding grains will be the rule. If the sand grains of the bed are uniform and not appreciably larger than those bombarding them, most of the saltating grains will "splash"—they will form little craters, perhaps burying themselves, but in the process will eject by their momentum one to several grains, which join the saltation. It would seem that the splash effect should be particularly characteristic of coastal dune sand, which is strikingly uniform in grain size.

The grains in surface creep receive their momentum by impact from the saltation, not directly from the wind. "Individual grains are knocked onward by the blow they receive from behind. At low speed they can be seen to move in jerks, a few millimetres at a time; but as the wind is raised, the distance moved lengthens and more grains are set in motion, till in high winds the whole surface appears to be creeping slowly forward . . . . Of the total weight of sand which flows past a fixed mark per second the surface creep accounts for between a quarter and a fifth" (Bagnold, 1941, p. 34). Saltation is thus responsible for most of the sand movement over the bed. The majority of the grains in saltation do not ordinarily rise more than 2–3 dm above the surface; a comparatively small number may attain a height of 1–2 m.

In the sand-carrying layer "saltation drag" (Bagnold, 1941, p. 102) reduces the velocity of the wind; there exists within it a general, though doubtless irregular, gradient from zero velocity at the surface of the sand bed to the speed of the general flow. An element of vorticity should be present, and sand in transport should increase small-scale turbulence. In spite of its thickness and complexity the sand-bearing layer approximates rather closely the concept of the boundary layer in the strict sense.

Development of the asymmetric profile with slipface.—It is assumed that, whatever the nature of its embryonic state, the transverse ridge is at an early point in its history approximately symmetrical in profile. It is further assumed that at this stage its convexity and the velocity of the wind are such that the sand-carrying "boundary layer" moves smoothly over its surface and maintains contact almost to the end. The flow is streamlined; there is essentially no separation. Saltation and surface creep operate throughout. Removal overbalances deposition on the windward slope because of local increase in wind velocity due to convergence of current threads, and the reverse is true on the leeward slope. The ridge progresses downwind without significant change in geometric form.

Asymmetry is initiated when separation first takes place, and separation, as we have seen, may be brought about in either of two ways: by increase of Reynolds number, geometric form being held constant, or by change in geometric form.[11] Increase of Reynolds number in turn may be effected either by increasing general wind velocity V or by increasing height L of the ridge. The first change may take place quickly, the second only through slow growth. When a certain higher value of Reynolds number has been reached separation will occur. With moderate increase the thick "boundary layer" becomes free, and because of the vorticity it has inherited will roll up into a weak stationary vortex. With further increase the free or vortex layer will move off downwind over a mass of stagnant air in the lee of the ridge. It will take a sinusoidal form, will roll up at intervals, and produce a procession of traveling vortices.

Separation will also occur with change of geometric form expressed in increase of convexity, wind velocity being held constant. Increase of convexity may be directly observed where a heap of sand lies on a hard surface. For such a case Bagnold (1941) has an explanation that seems entirely adequate. "A given wind can drive sand over a hard immobile surface at a considerably greater rate than is allowed by the loose sand surface . . ." (p. 72), since rebound is the rule instead of splash. Sand borne over a hard surface, unless the amount is very great, does not linger there. As soon as the sand-laden current passes across the boundary of a patch of sand, splash for the most part replaces rebound. Many of the bombarding grains bury themselves. The ejected grains reduce the velocity of the surface wind and therefore its transporting power. Accretion occurs; ". . . the dune grows fatter as it advances." In an earlier publication (1937) Bagnold thus summarized the process: "The growth of a dune need not depend on the deformation of the wind velocity distribution by the shape of the dune as an existing obstacle in the wind's path, but merely on a change of surface texture" (p. 437).

Observation shows that a surface of moist sand is similar to a hard surface in its effect on sand traveling over it by saltation. Little will linger; accumulation will take place when the sand-bearing current reaches a patch of dry sand. Again, the dune will grow fatter.

An important change occurs in behavior of the sand in transport after it passes the separation point. The grains in saltation must sooner or later drop out of the

---

[11] It is of course not implied that Reynolds number could be actually determined in field studies of dunes.

vortex layer (which goes on its way without them) and sink into the stagnant zone below. Most of the sand brought over the crest piles up just beyond the separation point, and the lee slope is thus locally steepened. The steepened face now extends itself down the slope and becomes steeper and longer as it progresses. As soon as the angle of slope at any point exceeds about 33° it becomes unstable, and the portion of sand involved slides down. An edge is thus produced, and separation henceforth takes

FIGURE 6.—*Profile of two transverse ridges, showing main air stream and dead air space* (ABC)
Vertical scale exaggerated

place there. Further sedimentation, which is followed by renewed sliding, occurs just below the edge. The slipface has come into being—in profile a straight line (except for temporary concavity at top due to oversteepening) with inclination from the horizontal of about 33° and angular juncture with the surfaces above and below.

The transverse ridge has now acquired the profile that will characterize it henceforth as it progresses with the wind. Assuming a theoretical pair of transverse ridges in equilibrium with constant environment and having level crest lines, the profile of the two at any given moment will be as in Figure 6. The current leaving the top of the slipface at A does not again strike the surface until it reaches C; from this point onward it is eroding the windward slope of the next ridge. In its upwardly deflected course erosion and transport are combined so that the windward slope advances downwind; C consequently advances downwind at a constant level. Since the area ACB is occupied by stagnant air, no further erosion of the surface BC can take place. BC is extended as C advances, and is invaded by the slipface AB; BC thus maintains constant width. In the ideal case a profile across the system will show a series of asymmetric ridges separated by level strips corresponding in breadth with the zones of stagnant air. In nature, of course, such perfect regularity never occurs. Deflected currents traceable to varying height of ridge crests and other irregularities tend to spoil the levelness of the interridge strips.

FIELD STUDIES OF WIND-CURRENT BEHAVIOR BY MEANS OF SMOKE

In the summers of 1940 and 1941 an attempt was made to discover the actual behavior of air currents in relation to various types of dune surfaces. Observation of the flight of sand is unsatisfactory because of its light color against a similar background, and because grains in saltation, although they derive their momentum from wind pressure, do not follow the current threads. Smoke particles, on the other hand, follow the current closely, and if dark in color stand out distinctly against a light background. Smoke has therefore frequently been used in investigation of the behavior of air currents, but mostly on a small scale in connection with experimental models. To provide the requisite volume, a "smoke candle," which produced a copious stream of black smoke enduring for 3 minutes, was used in these studies. Slow-motion cinematography provided a permanent record.

Before describing the experiments, the limitations of the method should be pointed out. The smoke stream, photographed from the side, gives only a vertical section. For this very reason, however, it is useful in being complementary to the two-dimensional treatment employed in the preceding section. Density of smoke prevents detection of details of air movement; only the major features are evident. The present study is admittedly crude. No adequate controls were established as to wind velocity and dimensions of ridges. But in spite of all shortcomings, significant results were obtained which strongly corroborate the points made in the theoretical discussion.[12]

The illustrations used here are enlargements from single frames of 16-mm movie film. Shots made with an ordinary camera stand a very slim chance of catching the exact moment that will be effective for illustration.

Figure 2A of Plate 8 shows the lee slope of a young, symmetrically rounded ridge. Perfect streamlining is evident. General velocity during the taking of this sequence was between 24 and 32 m.p.h. In Figure 2B of Plate 8 separation has taken place, but the slipface has not yet developed. Figure 2C of Plate 8 and the sequences, Figures 1 and 2 of Plate 9, depict behavior after appearance of the slipface. In Figure 2C of Plate 8 the vortex layer has a generally sinusoidal profile, but has begun to roll up at intervals. Succeeding frames show that a large vortex formed immediately. It is a rare occurrence to find the vortex layer so unbroken in continuity. It encounters many vicissitudes. It is often pushed downward by a violent descending gust; sometimes it rises well above its point of origin at the edge of the slipface. It is frequently distorted because of difference in velocity between adjacent current masses. Most commonly it is completely disrupted in longitudinal profile when portions of it roll up into large-scale vortices.

Two sequences have been selected from a considerable number to illustrate the behavior of the vortex layer. The pictures constituting these were made at the rate of 64 frames per second. For illustration every sixth frame has been taken, so that the photographs as presented here are approximately a tenth of a second apart. Each sequence represents 1½ seconds of time elapsed. The general wind velocity 1.5 m above the crest of the dune was about 20 m.p.h.

Certain general features are well shown by both sequences: rapid thickening of the vortex layer after separation, tendency toward sinusoidal profile both on a large and a small scale, gathering of smoke into dense knots. It is impossible to make out the type of movement at the points of densest concentration, but some of these may be traced downwind.

In Figure 1 of Plate 9 a knot which is first surely identifiable in frame 4 becomes a perfect ring in 9 to 12. Another may be followed through the last few frames until it becomes a ring in the final one. It is probable that the knots indicate centers of intense vorticity, some of which develop into well-formed major vortices. The principal

---

[12] Suggestion for further experimentation: smoke candles placed one above another at appropriate intervals, the series extending high enough to reach the region of general air flow. The experiments described here illustrate behavior only in a layer next to the sand surface about 1 dm in thickness. It is probable, however, that the sharpest part of the velocity gradient, and therefore the most intense vorticity, occur in this layer.

features in Figure 2 of Plate 9 are development of a large vortex culminating in frame 9 and the pushing downward of the vortex layer in the final frames.

Observation of the sequences with a projector shows that evanescent and imperfect vortices are constantly developing. The vortex layer is characterized by uninterrupted convection of vorticity downwind with production of well-developed vortices of various sizes at frequent and rather regular intervals. The large ones may be formed by coalescence of the smaller and imperfect ones. Bateman (*in* Dryden, Murnaghan, and Bateman, 1932, p. 220), drawing upon the work of Fujiwhara, states that "... two vortices with the same sense of rotation tend to approach ...", and that "... when the amalgamation of two vortices having the same sense of rotation takes place, the vortical motion gets new strength."

The space below the vortex layer, in which the air is almost stagnant, is invaded at infrequent intervals by minor gusts and eddies originating in the turbulent zone, which manifest themselves in feeble deflection of the vertical stream from a smoke candle set at the base of a slipface.[13] Sometimes a small whirlwind, carrying light particles of organic material and occasionally effecting slight local redistribution of the sand, will travel across the slipface.[14] During heavy winds a copious vertical shower of sand is constantly descending from the turbulent layer above.

"THE EDDY"—GENESIS AND PROPAGATION OF A FALLACY

The literature of dune phenomena abounds with references to an alleged major eddy which is supposed to maintain itself behind the lee slope of a transverse ridge or barchan, and to be very powerful in its effects upon their forms and movement. It is assumed to revolve upon a horizontal axis transverse to the wind direction. It has frequently been asserted, too, that in its backward and upward sweep it maintains or even increases the steepness of the slipface, and that it carries sand backward and upward to the top of the slipface into the main current.

In the present work theoretical conclusions have been verified by experiment for the coast of Oregon: that eddies occur abundantly but are powerless to affect the form or movement of transverse ridges to an appreciable degree. Form and movement are determined by the direct air current, whose threads curve and swerve but are free of true vortical motion. The transverse-ridge pattern of Oregon is duplicated the world over wherever there is deep sand and wind fairly constant in direction. If there is no effective posterior fixed eddy in the case of the Oregon dunes there should be none under similar conditions elsewhere. The "eddy" concept must therefore be taken

---

[13] Bagnold (1941, p. 209) makes the same observations with regard to the wind shadow in the lee of a barchan.

[14] Seligman (1936), investigating the behavior of wind currents in relation to formation of snow cornices, used smoke candles in connection with a small experimental ridge built of boards. In general his results appear to agree with mine. Seligman found, however, a steady upward current close to the lee slope of the ridge at the bottom but separated from it near the top by a calm area. Its velocity was about one-third of that of the main current, which had a speed of about 18 km per hour at the time. If such an upward current exists next to the slipface of a dune ridge it is too feeble to lift the sand or even seriously disturb it. It cannot be part of a fixed vortex, and is probably due to a pressure gradient.

as an unfortunate fallacy. Its history is a striking demonstration of the way in which an unproved concept becomes embedded in a body of scientific thought and of how it is transmitted from author to author until it finally reaches the textbooks. In the present case it is possible to trace the line of descent directly to its source—and that an innocent one.

1n 1884 Sir George Darwin published an important paper entitled *On the formation of ripple-mark in sand*. He dealt exclusively with water as the ripple-forming agent. By experimental methods he produced two types of ripples: oscillation ripples and current ripples, the former symmetrical in profile, the latter asymmetric or dunelike. Of current ripples he says (p. 34):

"The formation of irregular ripple-marks or dunes by a current is due to the vortex which exists on the lee of any superficial inequality of the bottom; the direct current carries the sand up the weather slope and the vortex up the lee slope. Thus any existing inequalities are increased, and the surface of sand becomes mottled over with irregular dunes."

Figure 2 on p. 23 of his work shows a fixed vortex occupying the whole depression between two adjacent ridges. It would be stated today that such a situation is the consequence of the particular Reynolds number determined by the experimental conditions. Darwin's work dealt with a definitely limited group of phenomena, and there is no apparent reason for questioning his results. Certain later authors have attempted to apply them in ways that are not justified.

Vaughan Cornish wrote extensively on dune phenomena as one phase of the "science of waves," which he termed kumatology, and it is his influence above all that has brought about general propagation of the concept of the eddy. In his first publication (1897) he stated that ". . . the stream-lines of air which give this shape [the asymmetric profile] to wind-ripples in sand may be inferred from fig. 2, which is Prof. G. H. Darwin's representation of the stream-lines when a current of water is made to flow over existing water-formed ripple-mark" (p. 280). Unqualified transference of principles of behavior from water to air is unwarranted, since a change in one of the terms of the equation for Reynolds number is involved; the kinematic viscosity of air is much greater than that of water—about 15 times as great at 20° C. It is of course possible to adjust the terms to obtain identical Reynolds number for air and water, in which case their patterns of flow will be the same. It may not be assumed that under ordinary conditions in nature Reynolds number, and therefore patterns of flow, will be the same for the two fluids.

A special phase of the eddy concept seems to have its root here: the alleged ability of the return current to lift solid particles to the crest of the ripple or the top of the slipface. Darwin in his experiments used ink as a tracer; he also observed ". . . minute particles [sand grains] lying on the surface of the sand climbing up the lee-slope of the ripples apparently *against* stream." This is entirely reasonable for Darwin's experiment with sand under water, but it is hardly conceivable that in air the return current of a fixed vortex, which is associated with very low general velocity, would have momentum sufficient to lift a sand grain to the top of a dune.

In a later publication (1900) Cornish made the direct statement ". . . the cliff [slipface] is due to undercutting by the backward-acting eddy." (p. 7) In his final and comprehensive work (1914) he described "the eddy" in detail. Two passages give the substance of his conception:

"On the lee side of each cliff [slipface] an eddy or vortex is active, a body of air which whirls vertically round a horizontal axis. At the crest the surface currents converge. Both currents are loaded with sand, which deposits on the lee side of the crest. At a position on the long, gently sloping weather side of the next wave the surface currents are, on the contrary, divergent, that at the tail end of the elongated vortex drawing sand back from the nodal position, whilst the direct wind, descending just above the node, drives the sand of all the upper part of the ridges forwards. Thus the upper part of each ridge is continually being scoured away and the eddy space to leeward is continually being filled up. By this process the position of each ridge continually advances to leeward, the core of eddying air being thus pushed forward, the progression of each successive core of eddying air permitting likewise the motion of the passive sand-waves." (p. 40–41)

"The measurements of sand-waves and sand-ripples showed their wave-length to be eighteen times as great as their height. If the node, or point of divergence of the surface currents, which is at the tail end of the eddy, be halfway between the trough and crest, then the length of the eddy is nine times as great as the height of the sand-wave and, as the height of the eddy cannot be much greater than the height of the sand-ridge, the eddy must be about nine times as long as it is high." (p. 180)

He adds that in a group of snow waves near Winnipeg ". . . the length of the eddy must have been about twenty-five times as great as the height." Vortices somewhat flattened are possible, but it is hard to conceive of such extreme cases as these, and impossible to imagine any combination of forces that in nature would cause the air current to turn the sharp corner required at the "node."

Many students of dunes have uncritically accepted the concept of the powerful lee eddy.[16] Dobrowolsky, who seems to have been the first to apply the principles of modern aerodynamics in the present field, apparently forgot the implications of these principles in applying them to dunes in nature. He stated (1924, p. 358) that ". . . it is the presence of a *fixed eddy back of the posterior slope* that constitutes the essential dynamic factor for every 'free' transverse dune." (italics are Dobrowolski's) Bourcart laid great stress on the importance of "the eddy", stating (1938, p. 200) that ". . . when the current is greatly accelerated there is produced, just this side of the point of impact of the current upon the ground, a horizontal eddy which exerts an erosion and ablation effect on the rear embankment." In consequence of this effect, he says, transverse dunes can progress but little; the lee slope is eroded about as fast as material is deposited upon it, and the sand from it is carried into the main stream, in which it will travel downwind to form new ridges.

Landsberg (1942), Landsberg and Riley (1943), and Rossby (1943) report on a study of wind-current behavior over a Lake Michigan sand dune. The locality chosen was a blowout trough, and a wind profile was constructed on its longitudinal axis by means of anemometers. Lakeward from the mouth of the blowout was a low foredune, "behind which a well-developed eddy [was] observed with wind motion next to the ground against the prevailing wind" (Rossby, p. 5). The complexity of the situation studied and the method used make interpretation uncertain.

During the period when Cornish was publishing his views there were a few authors

---

[15] Among them Bertololy (1900), Lomas (1907), Olsson-Seffer (1908; 1910), Cockayne (1911), Free (1911), Hahmann (1912), Bowman (1916), Bucher (1919), Högbom (1923), Dobrowolski (1924), Bourcart (1938).

who did not admit the effectiveness of a fixed eddy, though some of these assumed its general occurrence. Baschin (1903, p. 426) and Beadnell (1910, p. 387) believed that it cannot erode the lee slope. King (1918, p. 23) gave an essentially true picture:

"Below the layer of the wind on the lee side of the obstacle there is a space, roughly triangular in shape, of practically stagnant air, which however during a high wind is occasionally disturbed by small flaws. Between this triangular space and the current of air flowing over it small eddies a few inches in diameter frequently form during a gale."

King made crude observations on the behavior of smoke passing over a wall and could see no trace of a big eddy; he adds (p. 22): "Perhaps Dr. Cornish may have been misled by Darwin's theory of the small eddies that form in the troughs of ripples under water." In the discussion of King's paper several speakers expressed doubt as to the effectiveness of Cornish's eddy. Hume (1921) supported the views of King. These few expressions of dissent seem to have been submerged in the flood of papers by Cornish.

Most of the textbooks of geology confine themselves to the statement that the sand is carried over the crest and deposited on the lee slope. Five recent textbooks of geology and geomorphology, however, consider the lee eddy of importance (Lobeck, 1939, p. 383; von Engeln, 1942, p. 422; Cotton, 1949, p. 265, 266, 268; Garrels, 1951, p. 140, Fig. 6, 17; Kirkaldy, 1954, p. 92).

LEE-PROJECTION

This feature has been briefly described in a previous section; an explanation is here offered. A lee-projection is shown in Figure 3 of Plate 8; four smoke candles demonstrate the paths followed by the air currents that have formed it.

In the profile of Figure 6 level crest lines are assumed for the transverse ridges. In nature they are not so, but have alternating peaks and cols. The surface current from a summit will strike the windward slope of the next ridge at a higher level than that from a col. A transverse profile along the trend of the trough through any point in *BC* will therefore show elevations corresponding to high points to windward and depressions corresponding to cols.

The current lines of the surface wind converge in passing through the cols and fan out beyond. The latter process results in convergence of currents from the cols toward the areas behind the intervening summits. These currents cut into the swollen masses to leeward of the summits, narrow them, and steepen their lateral slopes. The result is a tonguelike residual structure behind each peak which is constantly developing downwind while its upwind end is being buried by the ridge following. The lateral cutting varies in degree; in some places it leaves a broadly rounded mass, in extreme cases a sharp-crested arête.

The lee-projection is thus an erosion remnant carved from the mass of a ridge that has progressed downwind. The beveled laminations usually showing on its eroded surface are clear evidence of this. In some cases it has a capping of fresh sand carried up its lateral slopes by the converging air currents. There is in many places a special accumulation at the juncture of the projection with the slipface, since the sand blown over the crest is here prevented from sliding down the full length of the slope. The crest in such cases rises toward the slipface.

An undulating crest line is essential for the production of lee-projections. In the strip next to the shore where the transverse-ridge pattern is best developed, this type of crest is the rule, and lee-projections are abundant. In the innermost areas of bare sand in Locality 19 the ridges are straight and very even-crested; lee-projections are extremely scarce.

An actual lee-projection is, of course, only an approximation to the ideal case presented above. Differences in configuration of the transverse ridges and variations in wind velocity and direction make for moderate diversity. For example, the low area represented by *BC* in Figure 6 is usually not absolutely level, one lateral slope of the projection may be steeper than the other, or the depression on one side may be deeper than the one opposite.

Since the lee-projections of the Oregon coast are characteristically erosion forms sculptured from moist coherent dune masses already in existence, it is not surprising that they rarely occur attached to isolated transverse ridges or barchans upon a hard substratum. Occasionally one is found associated with a small ephemeral ridge close to the shore. On other portions of the Pacific coast I have seen well-developed lee-projections in the Santa Maria region of southern California and in Baja California.

The lee-projection has received scant attention in the literature of dunes. Either it is uncommon or has been largely ignored. Cholnoky (1902, Fig. 5) gives a diagram of a barchan with a lee-projection. Examination of a number of published aerial photographs of barchans fails to reveal a single case. Cornish notes it briefly (1900; 1914) and in the latter publication attributes its formation to the action of "... an eddy, or a pair of eddies, with inclined or vertical axis on the lee of a peak." (p. 45) Beadnell (1910, p. 394) has seen " ... sand-tongues running out from the center of the crescent ... ", and agrees with Cornish as to their cause. Olsson-Seffer (1910) states that it is formed " ... by the combined action of the eddy in the lee and the current sweeping around the side of the dune." The present study shows that vortices are of no more importance here than in the development of the transverse ridge and its slipface.

ADDITION OF NEW MATERIAL

There is doubtless some inland movement from the beach throughout the year, but most of it must take place during the dry summer. The yearly amount is insignificant in comparison with the total accumulated mass, particularly because the summer winds strike the shore at a very acute angle. Much of the sand lifted from the beach settles upon it and returns to the water; the proportion that finds permanent lodgment on the dune sheet is small. Carrying of sand along the beach by wind constitutes a factor in longshore transport that has not to the author's knowledge been previously noted.

Before the advent of white settlers there was quite certainly no effective barrier between the upper beach and the dune sheet, and the sand passed directly from one to the other. There are places where this condition still exists. In most places, however, there is now an interrupted barrier built around driftwood—predominantly cut timber of enormous size—and clumps of marram grass. The resulting low sand ridge is a complex of partially coalescing tongue hills and plant mounds.

It is often stated that on a dune coast the sand is carried to the upper beach by the waves, dries out, and only then becomes subject to transport by wind. Some authors have asserted categorically that moist sand cannot be lifted by the wind (Sokolow, 1894; Cockayne, 1911, p. 9; Walther, 1924, p. 270). This is true neither for the beach nor for dune surfaces moistened by rain; Harlé and Harlé (1920, p. 67) and Landsberg and Riley (1943, p. 348) are emphatic on this point. Sand left wet by ebbing tide is almost immediately subject to removal. The process is clearly seen from a high point such as the mountain slope at the north end of the dune sheet (Pl. 10, fig. 1). When a gust strikes the surface, a white cloud suddenly appears, clearly outlined against the dark background of the moist sand, and moves off down the beach, very gradually approaching its inner edge. Such a cloud is shown at close range, looking upwind, in Figure 2 of Plate 10. It is 2–3 dm thick and exhibits a pattern suggesting anastomosing strands, which doubtless corresponds with an interweaving "fibrous" structure of the wind (cf. Langmuir, 1938). The rate of removal is rapid. In the period between tides every shell fragment becomes a capping for a pillarlike structure a few centimeters high, with a miniature tongue hill to leeward.

When and where velocity of the wind is reduced, the sand in transport, or some of it, is dropped. Special accumulations are formed in the lee of slight prominences, which here are poorly defined beach cusps. These, of course, survive only until the next flood tide.

The sand which is carried out of reach of the summer waves has a longer period in which to interact with the wind—a season instead of a few hours. Low accumulations come into being, at first apparently related to irregularities of the surface of the substratum. They soon merge into a festooned pattern with a tendency to develop strips transverse to the wind. These range from 2 to 6 m in width, and the spaces between them are on the order of 30 m.

Although the accumulations are only 1–2 dm deep, their profile is exactly the reverse of that characteristic of ripples and mature transverse ridges. The windward slope is very steep, the leeward very gentle. The steep windward slope progresses downwind and is constantly undermined by the air current impinging upon it. Part of the sand is carried over the top, but many grains fall back before reaching the summit. The sand blows from the gentle lee slope and flows along the surface of the substratum to the next strip. The stream from a smoke candle placed to windward maintains close contact with the surface of the strip from the base of the windward slope to the indefinite leeward boundary. No explanation of this apparent anomaly will be attempted. It may possibly be significant that the profile represents half of that of a typical streamlined obstacle immersed in a current with blunt upstream end and tapering tail.

As the accumulation grows in thickness, this type of profile is not maintained. The windward slope becomes less steep and proportionally longer until it and the lee slope are approximately the same. Further development is as described in an earlier section and culminates in the formation of a slipface. Rate of advance was measured for two small ridges which had developed slipfaces. One was 22 cm, the other 24 cm per hour. Wind velocity was 45 km per hour 1.5 m above the beach.

The complex has now become a system of anastomosing ridges with the typical asymmetric profile of maturity. As the ridges grow in magnitude the intervening bare spaces contract and finally disappear entirely. A miniature dune sheet has come into being, and the process suggests how any major dune sheet might have had its ultimate origin. An ample supply of sand is of course essential; otherwise the result would be merely a group of barchans.

The low accumulations take up water from the very moist substratum by capillarity; occasional rains add water from above. The bulk of the mass is constantly moist. After a heavy shower—which may occur even in the summer—the superficial part becomes particularly coherent and is subject to differential erosion. The wind cuts troughs which constantly enlarge until only scattered pillars are left. At the same time new ridges are developing. The old rhythm has been destroyed and another initiated; a new pattern comes into being amid the ruins of the old.

This miniature dune sheet is doomed to extinction at the end of the summer dry season, since it lies within reach of the winter storm waves. Before this happens, some of the ridges will have arrived at the edge of the main dune sheet. If no foredune intervenes they add their materials to it. The manner of incorporation is not clear. Since the ridges of the main mass are constantly progressing, new major ridges must take their place, and the sand for this must come from the beach. No gradual transition in size is apparent. The incipient ridges seem to lose themselves in the much larger ones of the main body. The problem can be solved only by constant observation at a particular spot.

Where a foredune or other barrier is present, addition of new material is less direct. The sand is first halted on the upper beach by formation of incipient ridges as described above. From these it is transferred to the zone of driftwood and strand plants, where it may remain for some time. Becoming disengaged from the influence of these obstacles, it moves inland and is incorporated with the mass of the transverse ridges which lie adjacent.

SEASONAL CYCLE

It has not been possible to observe personally the dunes during the winter season, when conditions are so different from those of summer. There is partial compensation in the fact that the first aerial survey was made on 2 days 7 months apart. Half of the area was covered on September 21, 1940, before the winter winds and rains had affected the summer pattern. The other half was photographed on April 20, 1941. On this date the topography due to winter conditions was still intact except for the barest beginnings of the pattern destined to reach perfection during the summer following. Three localities of special interest were photographed on both dates, so that direct comparison is possible in these areas.

The photographs show that the features developed during the summer are very much subdued in winter. The agents concerned are rain and wind. Rain alone has only a softening influence. Wind associated with wetness is the really powerful destructive agent.

Light rains in summer and early autumn thoroughly moisten the surface layer; this is soon worn through locally by the wind. Where there is dry sand beneath, a miniature blowout results. As it enlarges, the coherent surface layer collapses bit by bit. Sand set free by erosion of the moist surfaces collects in drifts which are very conspicuous against the dark background of moist sand. If no more rain falls for some days the wounds are healed, and the surface in general once more takes on the light tone of dry sand.

With repeated heavy rains percolation greatly increases the water content and coherence of the whole body, which is now subject to differential mass erosion. The sculpturing is in part determined by differing degree of coherence in the beds. A variety of forms results, often quite bizarre; detail of surface relief is temporarily increased (Pl. 10, fig. 3). The ridge crests, being most exposed, suffer most severely, and the sand blown from them, heavy with moisture, settles mainly in the depressions. The slipfaces develop crevasses, and great masses slump to the bottom. General relief is thus greatly decreased, and variability of the winds prevents development of any new pattern.

The extent to which the softening process is carried varies considerably, and the degree apparently depends upon relative exposure to the winter winds. Over much of the area, where elevation above sea level is appreciable, and no shelter is available, the transverse-ridge pattern is almost obliterated. Stereoscopic examination of the photographs reveals no relief. It seems hardly possible, however, that the transverse ridges are entirely destroyed. It is much more probable that they survive as low swells. A local resident describes the surface as gently rolling. The lee projections seem to disappear entirely. Near the shore, in very low areas protected by the rampart of the foredune, the transverse ridges persist through the winter, though much softened and minus their slipfaces. Rather surprisingly, the ridges are most perfectly preserved along the inner edge of the open sand at the north end of Locality 19. Here not only the ridges, but lee-projections survive, and the only modification is the usual softening of contour. This area lies at the base of the mountain front and would seem to be completely exposed to the violent southwest winds; but in such a situation there is probably a cushion of comparatively still air in front of the mountain slope, the main current being forced upward.

The embryonic stage in development of the summer transverse-ridge pattern and its relation to the pattern of the previous summer are shown in a pair of photographs covering a portion of the open expanse opposite Woahink Lake, Locality 20 (Pl. 11, fig. 1). Photo A was made on Sept. 21, 1940 and B on the following April 20. The distribution of dry sand on the latter date is the product of 3 days of strong northwest wind (5–7 on the Beaufort scale) after 4 days of rain. The pattern is made up of anastomosing strips of dry sand, roughly transverse to the wind, lying upon moist sand. The strips seem to be essentially of the same type as those which form in the summer on the upper beach during a few days of windy weather. They are probably low and streamlined in profile, without slipfaces. Near the shore they are rather narrow and are separated by broad bands of wet sand, the water table being close to the surface. Inland, the proportion of dry sand increases until it becomes an almost complete cover. The strips are still distinguishable, however, being separated by narrow, interrupted bands of moist sand. In many places they appear as if made up of closely interwoven strands, each of which is itself a very narrow strip of dry sand.

In the zone nearest the shore, and locally elsewhere, many strips can be definitely matched with transverse ridges of the previous September. Where accurate matching is impossible, the interstrip distance of April is closely comparable with the inter-ridge distance of September. It thus seems probable that in part at least the ridges of one summer are rebuilt upon foundations surviving from the summer preceding.

The history intervening between the embryonic stage of April and the conditions of summer may be interpolated by inference. The narrow interwoven strips of the inner zone coalesce into units equivalent to the outer single ones. All increase in thickness and acquire slipfaces. The process will be frequently interrupted by rains, but increasing dominance of north to northwesterly winds will prevent destruction of the growing forms. As the newly built ridges progress with the wind new lee-projections come into being. The characteristic pattern of summer has been reestablished.

The appearance of the dune sheet in summer might lead to the assumption that it is built entirely of dry sand. In reality the main body is moist throughout the year, and the superficial dry layer is thin. The latter increases in thickness through spring and summer, but very irregularly. During growth of new ridges, capillary movement and periodic rains add enough water to keep them moist. In summer the slipface deposits make the largest accumulations of dry sand, which during long rainless periods increase much faster than moisture can spread into them by capillary penetration. Walking the crest close to the edge of a slipface, one usually sinks ankle-deep and more into dry, incoherent sand. At the same time heavy winds may be exposing portions of the moist substratum on the windward slope.

SAND, WIND, AND WATER: THE OBLIQUE-RIDGE PATTERN

GENERAL NATURE OF THE PATTERN

The term oblique ridge has been adopted for the unit of the second pattern involving the elements sand, wind, and water to indicate its relation to the wind regime. It fits with neither of the orthodox categories, transverse dune and longitudinal dune.[16] Its trend is oblique to both the north-northwest wind of summer and the southwest wind of winter. Like the transverse ridge it does not occur alone, but constitutes a unit in a pattern based on repetition of parallel similar forms. Unlike the transverse ridge, it does not travel, but is fixed in position except for minor shifts with no consistent trend.[17] The massive, hard-surfaced basal portion, which is suggestive of the structure basal to the seif chain that Bagnold (1941, p. 229) terms the "plinth," is very stable. Vigorous sand movement is confined to the upper portion of the ridge. At their landward ends, in most series, adjacent oblique ridges are connected by a cross ridge, varying in height, so that the entire system takes the

---

[16] Search of the literature has revealed but one coastal area where a similar pattern seems to occur (Braun, 1911, p. 168). This is in Portugal. Braun's description is insufficient for a well-founded comparison, and aerophotos kindly provided by Mr. Francisco Flores indicate that the original pattern has been hopelessly obscured by recent planting operations.

[17] This generalization is confirmed by comparison of aerophotos made in 1940 and 1953, and through observations by Mr. C. O. Morgan of Winchester Bay, Oregon, who has watched the ridges of Locality 22 for 15 years.

form of a rake. The "cross bar" of the rake, consisting of the inner ends of the oblique ridges and the ridges that connect them, moves forward as a continuous front.

The oblique-ridge pattern on the Oregon coast is confined to a single area of dunes, albeit the greatest of all: the Coos Bay dune sheet, Region III, which extends 86 km along the coast. It occurs in all localities (nos. 19–23) grouped under this larger unit and provides the most spectacular features of the entire dune landscape.

MATURE OBLIQUE-RIDGE PATTERN IN LOCALITY 22

In the coastal strip between Tenmile Creek and the Umpqua River, the giant oblique ridges stand upon the seaward-facing slope of a bedrock ridge that lies parallel with the shore and rises to a maximum height beneath the dunes of 111 m. Bordering the shore is a level strip with well-developed transverse ridges. Landward from the active sand are older forested dunes undergoing invasion. Plate 18, figure 1 is a mosaic covering the entire locality; Plate 3 includes a tracing from it. Figure 2 of Plate 11 shows a part of the locality in summer and winter conditions. Figures 1 and 2 of Plate 12 present aspects of the oblique ridges in this area as viewed from the ground.

In length the ridges vary greatly; the average of 10 major ones is 1250 m; the length of the longest absolutely continuous one is 1700 m. They are highest at a point somewhat short of the landward end, both in absolute altitude and above the immediate base. Ridge A-A of Figure 7 at its highest point is 112 m above tide and stands 56 m above its base. The landward ends are bulging promontories (cf. Pl. 13, fig. 1; Pl. 3, Locality 20). Seaward from the highest points they become gradually lower and finally merge with the transverse-ridge pattern of the outer strip.

The ridges are spaced rather evenly, particularly in their outer parts, where average intercrest distance is about 180 m. Farther inland, spacing is less regular. Although they are sinuous in ground plan and differ one from another locally, a common trend is evident, most consistent in the outer portions, where the average of 18 ridges is N. 40° W., with an extreme range of N. 26° W.–N. 60° W. A short distance inland there is a common tendency to bend toward the east. Remnants of old stabilized dunes that survive in the midst of the sand sea cause deviation from the normal trend and in some cases complete interruption.

The floors of the interridge corridors lie for the most part close to or at the surface of the substratum. Where the latter is not actually exposed, proof of its near presence is afforded by iron-impregnated streamlets that emerge from the sand and flow on the surface until they are again absorbed, by ponds, and by small stands of young pine and a few spruces.

In summer the eroding northern slope is smooth-surfaced. The south side has a prominent slipface, below which is a gentler slope with firm surface that leads to the floor of the adjacent corridor or to the base of the next ridge south. Along the high inner portions the crest is a sharp ridge (Pl. 12, fig. 2), and in most places the compact windward slope is almost as steep as the slipface. Westward the summits become rounded, and transverse ridges climb upon their seaward ends.

A 2-day study in 1941 provided data concerning the winds of summer in relation to the oblique ridges. On September 6 and 7 (days typical of summer conditions)

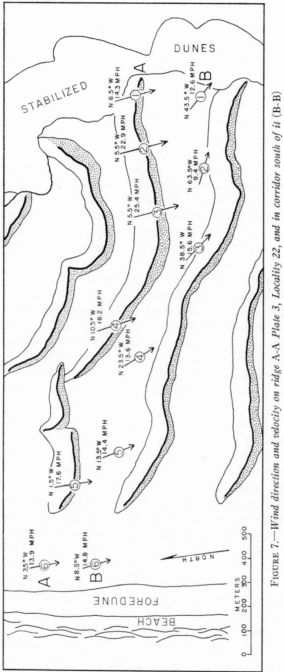

FIGURE 7.—*Wind direction and velocity on ridge A-A Plate 3, Locality 22, and in corridor south of it (B-B)*

Sept. 6 and 7, 1941

measurements of wind direction and velocity were made on an oblique ridge (*A-A* in Fig. 7) and in the corridor immediately south of it (*B-B*). On the first day six pairs of stations were occupied in two series, one along the crest of the ridge, the other in the corridor. The first pair was close to the landward ends of ridge and corridor, the last in the zone of transverse ridges beyond their seaward extremities. Wind velocity was measured by instruments of the type described in footnote 4. The summation period for each station was 30 minutes; stop and start at ridge and valley stations were simultaneous. The study began at 12:56 p.m. and ended at 5:38 p.m.; this period coincides closely with maximum velocity for the diurnal sea breeze. Wind direction was recorded at the start of the period and at intervals thereafter if significant variation was suspected.

Results of the study are shown graphically in Figure 7. Wind direction on the crest was quite uniform from end to end of the ridge; the total range was only 9° and the most westerly bearing in the middle. The average of the six stations was N. 5.5° W. At the innermost station direction fluctuated considerably, less at the next, and was steady for the remaining distance. In the valley, quite naturally, the air currents were deflected inland, the westerly component changing gradually from 8.5° at the shore station to 63.5° at Station 2. Velocity on the crest rose from 13.9 m.p.h. at the shore to a maximum of 25.4 m.p.h. at Station 3, then declined. These figures are averages for a 30-minute period; there were frequent gusts of much higher velocity. In the valley, velocities were much lower than on the crest and fairly uniform, the total range being 9.4–15.6 m.p.h.

Next day, September 7, comparison was made between the vicinity of the shore (Station 6) and the highest point on the ridge (Station 2). Wind direction at Station 6 was N. 11.5° E., which is 3° east of the coastal trend and thus actually, though very slightly, offshore. At Station 2 it was N. 18.5° W. Landward deflection at the ridge station in relation to the shore station was 30° as compared with only 2° on the preceding day. Anemometers were run simultaneously at two stations for a period of 60 minutes, starting at 3:35 p.m. The wind was decidedly stronger than on the preceding day; at Station 6 average velocity was 19.4 m.p.h., at Station 2, 29.8 m.p.h. On the crest of the ridge it was steady in direction but very gusty. From the valley *B-B* sand could be seen streaming from the crest of the ridge *A-A* in the vortex layer, making the well-known "smoke" effect. The slipface, about 12 m high, fed by gravity from the vortex layer, was plainly building southward at a rapid rate.

On the gentler compacted slope below the slipface the air was in a state of confused turbulence, its diverse movements made manifest by the behavior of the sand moving over the surface. Sometimes a wave of sand made up of grains in saltation advanced up the valley or down from the base of the slipface; occasionally directly up the slope. A gust striking the surface obliquely would cause the sudden appearance of a moving cloud of sand which vanished instantaneously as the gust subsided. An occasional blast struck vertically downward, producing the effect of an explosion. Vortices with vertical or oblique axes moved over the surface in various directions, usually downward toward the axis of the valley. The total effect of these actions upon the lower lee slope is that it is rasped smooth, producing firm rounded surfaces with all detail eliminated. On the windward slope of the next ridge south similar movements were observed, but the sand was more regular in behavior, traveling in waves and vortices obliquely up the slope with a strong landward component.

The oblique ridge in summer thus behaves essentially as a giant transverse ridge. The aerodynamic relations are the same in principle: geometric form, dimensions, and wind velocity determine the behavior of the air currents impinging on it (*see* Pl. 8., fig. 2 *B, D, E, F*). There is the same eroding windward slope and the same slipface to leeward. The body of air in the valley beneath the main current corresponds to the stagnant air mass in the lee of the slipface of an ordinary transverse ridge. Turbulence is more pronounced than in the latter but is erratic and, rather than controlling topography, is controlled by it. As with the ordinary transverse ridge there is no powerful fixed eddy in the lee of the crest.

For conditions in seasons other than summer there is only qualitative evidence. With beginning of the fall rains the moist sand becomes susceptible to sculptural erosion. South and southwest winds cut notches in the sharp summer crest and produce a sawlike profile in which the evenly spaced teeth may be 2 m high. Winds from other directions partially undo the work of the southwesterlies, and during winter the crest is cut down and broadened into a flattish strip as much as 25 m wide (Pl. 11, fig. 2B). Considerable quantities of sand are carried northward, even in the midst of rain. Some flies off horizontally from the crest, but most pours over the crest and down the lee slope. A slipface of a sort forms on the north side which is subject to frequent mass slumping. Thus in winter, too, the ridge behaves as a transverse ridge; its faces are reversed, and differences in behavior are due to the water factor. In spring, with decrease of precipitation and increasing dominance of northerly wind, the characteristics of summer are gradually restored.

MAINTENANCE OF THE OBLIQUE-RIDGE PATTERN

It is clear that the oblique ridges, whatever their ultimate origin, owe their maintenance to interaction of two winds seasonally alternating. The summer northerlies at a given point on the coast are very constant in direction; the winter southwesterlies are more variable. For the sake of simplicity in analysis each may be treated as directionally constant and resolved into two components with respect to the ridge trend: forward and lateral. The former brings about sand movement ahead and furnishes material for extension of the ridge; the latter sweeps the sand from the corridors and concentrates it in the ridges.

Explanation of the precise trend acquired by a ridge requires knowledge of more than wind direction, even though resolved into components. Frequency, duration, and velocity combined determine the competency of the wind in transport of sand, and the relative competencies of summer and winter winds share in determination of the trend. Data adequate for satisfactory quantitative treatment are nonexistent for the Oregon Coast—or any other dune region. An approximation of the situation may, however, be attempted. In Figure 8 the point A is assumed to represent the advancing terminus of the oblique ridge, the point where its trend is established. AB is the average trend of the oblique ridges between the Umpqua River and Coos Bay (Localities 22 and 23) in their outermost parts. AC and AD indicate the mean directions of high-velocity winds (16 m.p.h. and over) of summer and winter respectively, derived by rough computation from the data for North Bend, the nearest weather station. These directions may be taken as known quantities; the relative competencies of the two winds are still to be determined. Applying the principle

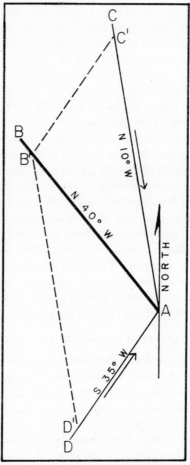

FIGURE 8.—*Average trend of oblique ridges in localities 22 and 23 and mean directions of summer and winter winds 16 m. p. h. and over at Coos Bay*

A: advancing terminus of ridge. *AB:* trend of ridge. *AC:* Summer wind. *AD:* winter wind. Parallelogram of forces (*AC′B′D′*) gives relative efficiency of the seasonal winds in determining the trend of the ridge.

of the parallelogram of forces, *AC′* and *AD′* become vectors in which direction and relative competency are integrated. *AC′* is about twice as long as *AD′*; the competency of the summer wind in transport of sand is thus about twice that of the winter wind. Their joint competency in moving sand along the trend of the ridge is indicated by the length of the diagonal *AB′*.

As long as the two vectors remain unchanged in every respect, the ridge must continue to extend itself in the direction indicated by the line *AB* and at a constant rate. Introduction of a change in one of the vectors, in direction or in length, will result in a change in direction and length of the diagonal AB'. The advancing terminus of the ridge will take a new direction, and the ridge will extend itself at a new rate. For example, the consistent change in trend of the oblique ridges in Locality 22, a short distance inland, from N. 40° W. to an average of about N. 63° W., already noted, might be brought about either by shifting vector AC' from N. 10° W. to N. 32° W., with relative competencies unchanged, or by changing the relative competencies of summer and winter winds from 2:1 to 1.25:1, leaving directions unchanged. The trend of the ridge is determined primarily at its advancing terminus, but minor changes may occur farther back due to local alteration of direction and velocity of the wind caused by topographic features such as neighboring ridges, remnants of older dune masses, and even the ridge itself.

Assuming adequate sand supply, the ridges extend themselves inland. Forest is not an insuperable obstacle, but it does decrease the rate of progress. In the big ridges of Locality 22, sand is brought to their inner ends in quantity greater than can be cared for by advance of the ridges against the forest. The inner extremities in consequence become massive promontories (*cf*. Pl. 13, fig. 1). Measurements at the toe of the ridge A-A in Figure 7, from 1945 to 1951 inclusive, demonstrated advance at an average annual rate of 1.63 m. If the substratum were free of obstacles the ridges would extend themselves more rapidly than they do and would presumably taper to a point.

PROBABLE ORIGIN AND DEVELOPMENT OF THE PATTERN

It is far easier to describe the oblique-ridge pattern and even to explain how it is maintained in its mature state than it is to discover its origin and predict its future. Nowhere is it possible to observe oblique ridges in embryonic state. In Locality 23 there are, however, clues pointing to one way in which they may come into being. There is here a lengthy series of oblique ridges lying near and parallel to the beach (Fig. 9). It is somewhat interrupted, and the ridges are relatively small and obviously young. Associated with them and attached to some at their inner ends is a precipitation ridge[18] whose slipface is invading a young pine forest growing on a low, flat deflation surface. Shoreward from the oblique ridges and interfingering with them is a zone reduced essentially to deflation base,[19] in summer partly covered by a thin sheet of mobile sand marked by the transverse-ridge pattern. Finally, at the top of the beach is a foredune composed of thickly placed hillocks bound by marram grass. The length of the most extended ridge in 1941 was 500 m; the tallest rose 27 m above its base. The trends of 26 ridges ranged from N. 30° W. to N. 59° W., and the average was N. 40° W. (significantly, the same as in Locality 22). In summer the ridges are smooth-contoured, and there is a slipface on the south side. In winter the form is less regular; there is an imperfect slipface on the north side.

Development of this situation is visualized as follows. There is in the outer deflation zone abundant evidence, consisting of dead pine trunks, willow bushes, and

---

[18] A ridge due to precipitation of sand at a forest edge.

[19] The level deeper than which removal of sand cannot go under existing conditions, usually set by the water table.

exposures of a weak soil horizon, that in the rather recent past the forest extended seaward at least as far as the outer ends of the ridges, perhaps almost to the present beach line. (The foredune did not then exist since it is due entirely to recent introduction of marram grass.) Because of change in conditions—cause unknown—there

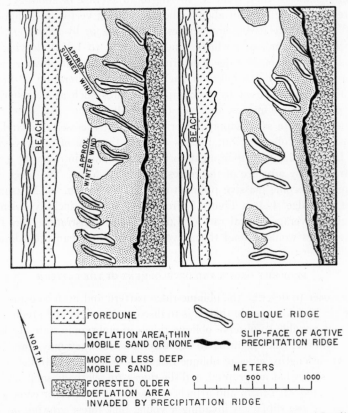

FIGURE 9.—*Youthful oblique ridges associated with the outer active system of Locality 23*
From aerophotos made April 20, 1941

was increase in amount of sand carried inland by the wind. Had there been nothing to hinder its advance, it would have spread out as an even sheet and acquired the transverse-ridge pattern. But it encountered an obstacle in the forest, and a precipitation ridge, parallel to the shore, came into being, moved inland, destroyed the forest, and gradually increased in height. Figure 3 of Plate 12, although it does not represent actual initiation of oblique-ridge formation, suggests its manner. Deposition was naturally not uniform on the precipitation ridge. Extra sand accumulated at certain points due perhaps to irregularities in the forest barrier. Advance inland was more rapid where the ridge was low, and the bulkier masses thus tended to be left behind. Such a bulging mass, if substantial enough to escape destruction in its first few years, had a good chance of developing into a unit structure in its own right. Lag in relation to landward advance of the adjoining lower portions of the precipitation ridge brought about its conversion from a formless mound into a ridge with flanks open to the oblique impact, alternately, of the northerly winds of summer and the southwesterly gales of winter. In summer, sand was carried obliquely up the northern slope and over the crest, most of it falling on the southward-facing slipface. In winter, sand passed obliquely over to the north side, most of it remaining on the ridge. Crossing and recrossing the crest, the sand pursued a zigzag landward course, following the trend of the ridge, thus contributing to its nourishment and extension. As the ridges grew in bulk through absorption of the mobile sand, the interridge corridors suffered depletion; their floors were lowered, in places to deflation base.

Several detached ridge segments lying outside the main system seem to indicate decrease in sand supply from the shore since the system came into being. Certain of the ridges, becoming attenuate at a point, were cut through, and their seaward portions were left isolated. The latter, barring increase of sand supply, will be gradually reduced until their materials are completely dissipated. Even those oblique ridges that have maintained contact with the precipitation ridge seem to have been wasting away at their seaward extremities, so that they have shifted bodily inland. The prospects for this particular system, after a good start, seem none too favorable.

The massive system in Locality 22 may well have had a similar origin and history. The early precipitation ridge here, however, soon encountered, instead of a flat deflation plain, a slope deeply mantled with sand accumulated during a long, complicated history of dune building and thoroughly stabilized by mature forest. The precipitation ridge swept inland and destroyed the forest cover. Its advance was not regular; bulkier masses were left behind as tree-crowned "peninsulas". Erosion, cutting in laterally, converted portions of the peninsulas to "islands", some of which still survive. Stripping of the forest cover eliminated the factor vegetation, leaving sand, wind, and water as the phases of the system. In the reworking of the sand mantle that now lay almost completely exposed, the pattern of massive oblique ridges, already established near the shore, extended itself inland. There has been no sand starvation here. In addition to the enormous amount of older material immediately at hand, new sand has been available in considerable abundance because of proximity to the open mouth of the Umpqua River. The ridges in their inland extension have consequently attained enormous size.

The hypothesis suggested above—that the existing systems of oblique ridges originated in precipitation ridges close to the shore and extra-large masses served as nuclei for development of oblique ridges—is supported by the general occurrence throughout the Coos Bay dune sheet of oblique ridges in series and the binding together of their landward ends in a common advancing front. Their quasi-regular spacing may be accounted for by disintegration of the smaller masses or their absorption by the larger ones. Other possible causes of initial accumulation are, of course, not excluded. Additional conditions essential for development of the oblique-ridge pattern are exposure to the full force of both summer and winter winds, an adequate supply of new sand from the shore, and space to extend itself inland, level or not abruptly sloping. Once firmly established, it may maintain itself for a very long time even though the supply of new sand ceases. The Coos Bay dune sheet is favorable in its wide coastwise extent which gives unobstructed access to both seasonal winds, in a continuous flat littoral strip, and in a copious supply of fresh material from the Siuslaw and Umpqua Rivers. Absence of oblique ridges in other dune localities may be accounted for by lack of some or all of the above conditions.

DECLINE OF THE OBLIQUE-RIDGE PATTERN

Instability of the pattern.—There are strong indications that the oblique-ridge pattern, stable as it seems to be, will not maintain itself indefinitely against certain powerful factors that oppose it individually or in combination: sand starvation, invasion by transverse ridges, and vegetation.

Sand starvation.—Failure of sand supply at the shore, partial or almost complete, has occurred many times and at many places on this coast; the causes are little understood. It acts directly on the oblique ridges, and may become effective very early, as on the outer system in Locality 23. It is related to the other two factors in opposite ways: meager sand supply weakens or halts attack by transverse ridges but is prerequisite to establishment of vegetation that will encroach upon and in time eliminate the oblique ridges.

Attack by transverse ridges.—The transverse-ridge and oblique-ridge patterns are in competition. Field study and examination of aerophotos give the impression that wherever the two patterns overlap, the transverse ridges have the upper hand, ephemeral as they are in comparison with the huge structures of the other pattern. While the landward extremities of the oblique ridges are extending themselves, the seaward ends seem to be shrinking, even where sand supply is abundant. The shrinking process, if authentic, is due to invasion of the outer ends of the oblique ridges by transverse ridges moving in from the shore. Since the latter are active only under influence of the summer winds, they move obliquely across the outer ends of the oblique ridges and carry much sand southward and southeastward that would otherwise follow a zigzag course along the trend of the oblique ridge. The smooth-contoured, sharp-crested form determined by cross winds is gradually transformed into a rounded mass fanning out southward and covered completely by transverse ridges of great size. These are at first irregular, but gradually develop the parallelism characteristic of the pattern. The final result is reduction to the general level, with transverse ridges over all.

Supersession of oblique ridges by transverse ridges is most apparent in Locality 20 (Pl. 19, fig. 2). The oblique ridges form a continuous series along the inner margin of the active sand. They are comparable in mass to those of Locality 22, but are shorter and farther apart. Between them and the shore is a flat deflation zone 1–2 km wide completely covered by transverse ridges.[20] It is assumed that here, as in the preceding localities, the oblique-ridge pattern was initiated near the shore at a time when forest extended almost to the beach. Sand supply is copious because of the continuously open Siuslaw River a few kilometers to the north, and as the oblique ridges advanced inland they acquired additional material from destruction of older dunes. The constantly widening deflation zone has been completely overspread by transverse ridges, which prevent development of a vegetation cover. These have

---

[20] The principal locality utilized in study of this pattern.

fed a certain amount of new sand to the oblique ridges, but their principal effect upon the latter has been degradation of their outer ends. Because this process is more rapid than headward extension, the oblique ridges have become gradually shorter.

A persisting remnant of old stabilized dune may act as a protecting buttress and temporarily halt shrinkage of the ridge behind it. In Figure 1 of Plate 7 the dark mass with the long shadow is such a remnant. Its protection seems to have failed quite recently, for immediately to the rear the ridge has suffered degradation through invasion by transverse ridges of great size, which, moving southward, have produced the usual fan configuration. In 1940, the date of Figure 1 of Plate 7, these were very irregular; by 1953 parallelism had been attained. A series of annual measurements[21] at the foot of the slipface of the most advanced of these ridges (Pl. 13, fig. 2), from 1947 through 1950, showed southward progress at the very high rate of 5.5 m per year. The spruce in this figure rose 10 m above the sand in 1940; by 1946 it was almost completely buried. The inner part of the ridge in 1940 was sharp-crested and rose 49 m above its base, and the slipface itself was 36 m high. In 1953 this crest had been lowered an unknown but considerable amount, and the appearance of lee-projections where the high smooth slipface had been was a further sign of degradation.

South of the remnant mentioned above there are visible in Figure 1 of Plate 7 two oblique-ridge segments that have lost their landward portions. The northern one is clearly recognizable as an oblique ridge with a definite slipface on its southern aspect; the southern is a mere elongate swell completely overrun by transverse ridges. Both show plainly the fanlike southward spread at their seaward ends, and both underwent a perceptible amount of degradation in the interval between 1940 and 1953.

There is evidence that the trend toward degradation may sometimes be reversed. Southwest of Cleawox Lake (Locality 20) a group of subdued linear swells, oriented and spaced like oblique ridges but almost completely masked by a system of transverse ridges, had been assumed to be dying oblique ridges overcome by the competing pattern. Two of these swells had, however, in the period 1940–1953 developed definite, continuous crests. In Locality 22 several oblique ridges extended themselves seaward a short distance during the same period. The conclusion seems to be that the transverse ridges have in general the advantage.

Encroachment by vegetation and final extinction of the oblique ridges.—In order that vegetation may play its role, a period of sand starvation long enough to permit development of forest on a deflation surface seaward of the ridge system is prerequisite. This has happened in Locality 23, where an old series of comparatively short but massive oblique ridges stands at the inner edge of the dune sheet (Pl. 3, Locality 23). In its early stages the system must have received its supply of sand from the shore. A period of meager supply prevented development of the transverse-ridge pattern on the deflation surface; vegetation took over and isolated the system from its source of nourishment. With increasing distance from the shore, and growth of

---

[21] Carried out by Mr. C. O. Morgan.

forest to windward, there has been decrease in force and regularity of the winds, and the ridges have lost much of their earlier sharpness of sculpturing.

Field evidence is lacking as to the final stages of decline of such a system. Everywhere the ultimate stabilized form is the precipitation ridge. It would seem that the active oblique-ridge system must finally be converted into that form, for during previous advances that culminated in stabilized precipitation ridges, oblique-ridge systems like those of today must have been present. The most reasonable assumption is that the shrinkage of the oblique ridges already indicated continues until they merge with the cross ridges that bind together their inner ends, producing a massive, simple precipitation ridge. Forest, invading from the deflation plain, finally spreads over all. Details of the forest invasion are given later in the section "Further history of the precipitation ridge."

"OBLIQUE RIDGE" AND "LONGITUDINAL DUNE"

In the course of this inquiry into the nature of the oblique ridges on the Oregon coast and the factors involved in their development, the fundamental similarity of these structures to the "longitudinal dune" of desert regions, in spite of conspicuous superficial differences, has become apparent. The study given to the oblique-ridge pattern has led to formulation of a hypothetical explanation of the "longitudinal dune" pattern in general, which is offered here with the hope that it may be tested in other regions where and when adequate data become available. It is based on fact and theory derived from the Oregon dunes but finds considerable support in the work of certain recent students of desert dunes.

The customary statement that the trend of longitudinal dunes corresponds to the prevailing wind direction contains an element of truth, but in ignoring or minimizing the possible influence of other winds it is seriously misleading.[22] In any attempt to explain a dune pattern the entire wind system of the region must be considered. The present hypothesis states that for the development of a pattern of "longitudinal" dunes cross winds, converging upon the unit ridge at angles which may vary greatly, are essential. Winds strictly parallel to the trend of the ridges have a share in transport of sand, but are not indispensable. A brief survey of outstanding examples of the longitudinal-dune pattern as they appear in the literature will be followed by elaboration of the hypothesis just stated.

An example frequently cited in textbooks is from the great desert of the Indus Valley in Pakistan; it is described in an early work by Medlicott and Blanford, rewritten by Oldham (Medlicott and Blanford, 1893). In this region with its regime of monsoon winds longitudinal dunes are said to prevail near the coast and transverse ridges inland. Available data are not adequate for detailed discussion.

The longitudinal dune chains of the Egyptian-Libyan Desert have been described by a number of authors. Speakers in discussion of a paper by King (1918) suggested that the "shepherding effect" of winds blowing upon either quarter may be important in development of a longitudinal dune, and Hume (1921) noted the idea

---

[22] The authors of a very recent textbook (Leet and Judson, 1954) recognize the difficulty: "It is difficult to understand how a wind of constant direction can account for the initiation of longitudinal dunes." (p. 233)

with approval. The most careful study is that by Bagnold (1941), who employs for the unit segment the Arabic word *seif*. Series of these mounds are joined end to end to form a seif chain. A single chain may run without interruption for 100 km, successive chains in line for much greater distances. "Each chain has a broad massive stern to windward and its leeward end dwindles to a sharp point." (p. 229) Many summits attain a height of 100 m. The chains are remarkably straight for long distances. They are plainly under the general control of the continental trade winds; their trends swing around from north-northwest in the north to west-southwest in the south. Lateral shift of the chains seems to be negligible. The interridge corridors are 1 km to as much as 10 km wide and are swept almost bare of sand.

Bagnold shares the difficulty encountered by the present writer in explaining emergence of the form *ab initio*. He suggests the possibility of origin from a barchan formed by a gentle wind, subjected periodically to an oblique cross wind of greater strength (Bagnold, 1941, p. 223, Fig. 78).

Bagnold's discussion, like mine, deals mainly with the maintenance and extension of the ridge or chain. It is evident that he considers winds from at least two directions essential to the existence of a seif chain: "The longitudinal or seif dune occurs when the wind regime is such that the strong winds blow from a quarter other than that of the general drift of sand caused by the more persistent gentle winds." (p. 195) The gentle wind ". . . drives sand off a dune on to the surrounding country, causing the dune to extend down-wind in the process." (p. 186) This is presumably the general drift of the trade wind and determines the trend of the chain. The other wind, relatively strong, ". . . causes an accretion of more sand upon a sand surface. It is the dune-building wind." (p. 186) It sweeps the sand from the corridor areas and concentrates it in the chains. While it is in action, a slipface develops on the leeward side of each summit, parallel to the trend of the chain.

Bagnold states further (p. 224) that ". . . in some areas the directions of the storm winds are such that storms blow towards the dune from either side of the main resultant axis." In such a case ". . . the slip-face is a temporary phenomenon which is formed and reformed on either side according to the direction from which the cross-wind happens to blow." (p. 225) The strong likeness of this situation to conditions on the Oregon coast is obvious.

In the great ergs of the Algerian Sahara are systems of dune chains apparently equivalent in fundamentals to those of the Egyptian-Libyan desert. Like the latter, they are clearly controlled by the continental trade winds. Aufrère (1931; 1933; 1935) offered an explanation of "longitudinal chains" that is very different from that of Bagnold; in part it had been previously suggested by Cornish (1908). He believed that the longitudinal chains develop from a system of transverse ridges (1933, p. 705). The wind passing through a col in a transverse ridge reduces the corresponding portion of the next ridge. Cols and summits thus tend to align themselves in the direction of the wind. From such small beginnings gradually develops a system of chains and corridors aligned with the trade winds. The pattern is maintained because greater wind velocities develop over the corridors than over the ridges. Capot-Rey (1945, p. 404) and R. and F. Capot-Rey (1948, p. 75) point out that Aufrère's explanation is at fault (1) in that it does not take into consideration the entire wind system and (2) in that emphasis is put upon frequency to the exclusion of other characteristics: velocity and turbulence.[23]

The ergs of the Australian deserts, described by Madigan (1936; 1946) exhibit a longitudinal-ridge pattern probably surpassing all others in continuity and regularity, though inferior to the Saharan ergs in amount of sand involved. Here again the ridges are aligned with the trade winds. They are straight, continuous for hundreds of kilometers, and to a degree evenly spaced. Their maximum height is only 30 m, and the average 12. The interridge corridors average 400 m in width and are almost bare of sand. The ridges are advancing to leeward and undergoing very slow destruction at their windward ends. The lower slopes are stabilized by sparse desert vegetation, but the crests are open and bear small crescentic dunes that vary in orientation with winds that cross the ridge trend.

Madigan (1946) traces the origin of the ridges of the Simpson Desert to small sand strips parallel to the strong southerly winds. "Suitable southerly winds will extend the strip down-wind.... Strong side winds will build up the whole length of the strip, increasing its height and bulk.... When it reaches a certain height it will become an obstacle that will arrest all sand driven by side winds at whatever angle, so that the lanes between strips may be swept free of sand." (p. 59)

In the Navajo-Hopi country of northeastern Arizona there are a number of areas of limited extent bearing parallel longitudinal ridges similar to those of the Australian deserts. They are, however, on a far lesser scale. The individual ridges are not more than 8 km long, the maximum height is 10 m, and the distance apart about 100 m. They are like the Australian ridges in that the lower slopes are partially stabilized by vegetation whereas the crests are bare. The trend is uniformly southwest to northeast. They have been described by Melton (1940) and Hack (1941).

Melton in his classification of sand dunes includes the Arizona ridges (and apparently all other "longitudinal" dunes) in his category of "wind-shadow dunes" behind permanent bedrock obstacles (p. 120). On the Moenkopi Plateau, the ridges are initiated "... above and behind the promontories which lie between headward-eroding canyons of the cliff face." (p. 121) The cliff lies athwart the prevailing southwest winds. "Unvarying wind direction is, of course, essential to the formation of longitudinal dunes of the Moenkopi type. Variations of 1–2 degrees in prevailing wind direction, if continued for only short periods, would trim the dune extremities and shorten them very rapidly." (p. 121)

Hack (1941, p. 258–259) gives a very different picture but attempts no detailed explanation. According to him the wind picks up sand from the gullies. At the top of the cliff on the plateau a dune mantle comes into being, semistabilized by vegetation and showing parabolic forms. "The excess sand blowing from the parabolic dunes is extended for two to five miles to leeward as long active longitudinal dunes. Still farther back, the plateau is covered by longitudinal dunes that are more or less stabilized." (p. 259)

Students of three great regions of longitudinal dunes, Bagnold, Capot-Rey, and Madigan, thus recognize the importance of cross winds in the regions in which they

---

[23] The two contributions by Capot-Rey and Madigan's later report on the Australian ridges are adequately reviewed by Price (1950).

have worked. It would seem, then, that the relation must be a general one: that winds oblique to the ridge trend are essential, through their lateral components, for concentration of sand in the ridge.

For the Oregon dunes it is convenient, and legitimate as well, to assume two controlling winds, even though each is made up of an infinite number of theoretical wind units differing in direction, duration, and velocity. The angle between the two is very obtuse; in Figure 8 it is taken as 135°. The lateral components are very powerful in comparison with the forward ones. Concentration of sand in the ridges dominates over forward transport; the ridges increase in bulk but extend themselves slowly. There is, as has been pointed out, an additional obstacle to lengthwise extension not found in the desert—the forest front.

For regions where satisfactory data are not available it is still possible, in theoretical treatment, to separate the wind units into two groups, those impinging on the ridge from the right and those from the left, and to consider the theoretical resultants of each of these as two simple oblique cross winds. The angle between them may vary widely. If it is wide, as on the Oregon coast, massiveness is emphasized rather than extension. The narrower the angle, the greater the effectiveness of the forward components; the more rapidly the ridge will extend itself, but at the expense of bulk. As the angle becomes more acute, maintenance of the longitudinal-ridge pattern should continue until the lateral components become too feeble for effective concentration of the sand in the ridges. With approximation to unidirectional wind, and sand moving straight ahead, the transverse-ridge pattern appears if the deposit is deep; if it is scanty, a flock of barchans.[24]

Occasional winds strictly in line with the ridge trend contribute to its extension by transport of sand both along the ridge itself and along the adjacent corridors, in the latter case to be incorporated in the ridge by a cross wind at a later time. Winds from other directions have, of course, their effects. Winds in opposition to those that dominate will decrease the rate of extension; they may, however, striking the ridge at an angle, aid in concentration of the sand therein.

The systems of longitudinal dunes in subequatorial deserts owe their character to a regime in which winds from many directions play a part. The prevailing winds, the trades, in a general sense are constant in direction. The forward component is always predominant and accounts for the tremendous extension of the ridges. There must be, however, variation in direction of the trades sufficient to provide at times a lateral component powerful enough to cause transfer of sand from corridor to ridge. There are also the strong cross winds mentioned by Bagnold, in which the lateral component may be as great or greater than the forward. The only difference between Bagnold's analysis and mine is that Bagnold attributes concentration of sand in the ridges solely to cross winds distinct from the dominant trades and ignores the contributions made by currents converging at a narrower angle.

For the Australian deserts Madigan in his earlier publication (1936, Fig. 2) provides a map with wind roses for all available stations fairly close to the sand-ridge deserts. The most frequent wind direction for a given station (the southeast trade wind) is shown to agree well with the trend of the ridges in the vicinity. But at the

---

[24] Bagnold, 1941, p. 195: "The barchan dune . . . . occurs when the wind is nearly uni-directional."

nine stations closest to the dune fields frequencies agreeing with the trend range only from 27 to 46 per cent of the total frequencies and average about 33 per cent.[25] The remaining frequencies cannot be ignored. Another average 25 per cent fall within the octants to right and left of the dominant octant, and these must contribute effectively both to concentration of sand in the ridges and to their extension. Only an average 12 per cent are in direct opposition. Madigan, particularly in his later publication, does not ignore winds other than the dominant: in various parts of the Simpson Desert ". . . the trend varies with the resultant of all sand-driving winds." (1946, p. 60)

Reconciliation of the present hypothesis with Aufrère's concept is impossible, but Capot-Rey's discussion brings the situation in the Algerian Sahara into line.

The concept here presented is in direct opposition to the contention of Melton that a variation of "a degree or two" in prevailing wind direction must be fatal to extension, even to the existence, of a longitudinal ridge. Melton offers no evidence that the southwest winds of northern Arizona possess so astonishing a degree of constancy in direction. He admits the existence of other winds, but holds that ". . . wind may blow from various directions and still not move an appreciable amount of sand or reconstruct dune topography greatly." (1940, p. 115) The question is surely a fair one: if deviation of 1°–2° is such a serious threat to the longitudinal dune, why should winds from radically different directions be ineffectual?

For the Oregon dunes a theoretical analysis of the causes determining the precise trend of the oblique ridges has been presented. It seems reasonable that in other systems of similar character, including the longitudinal dunes of the subequatorial deserts, the underlying principles are the same. One conspicuous difference should be noted. The antagonistic factors—sand starvation, attack by transverse ridges, vegetation—that tend to limit the life span of the oblique ridges on the coast of Oregon are absent or quite ineffective in the deserts. Therefore the longitudinal dunes of the deserts should maintain themselves indefinitely—as long as the climate retains its desert character, and the wind system remains essentially unchanged.

It seems quite proper, for these deserts, to speak of the ridge trend as parallel to the dominant winds, of the ridges as longitudinal dunes, provided that the importance of the entire wind system in their control is clearly recognized.

SUMMARY: THE TWO PATTERNS

Two patterns developed through interaction of sand, wind, and water have been discussed. A brief synthesis is here offered.

The transverse-ridge pattern occurs in every major dune locality south of Tillamook Head. It is controlled solely by the north to northwest winds of summer, and the ridges advance before them. Other essential conditions are a terrain level or without abrupt change in gradient and free of significant obstacles, and a supply of new sand sufficiently ample and constant to prevent exposure of the substratum or reduction to deflation base. The pattern is partially destroyed in winter and rebuilt in summer.

The oblique-ridge pattern is confined to the Coos Bay dune sheet, because only here are all the requisite conditions met: full exposure to both the seasonal winds

---

[25] The percentages have been derived from measurements of Madigan's wind roses.

that control it, plenty of space, and plenty of sand. The units of the pattern are massive and widely spaced. The trend of the unit ridge lies between the means of summer and winter winds, and the ridges, in contrast with those of the other pattern, hold an essentially fixed position. Once firmly established, the pattern is long-lived, especially where abundant material from older dunes is available for reworking. Factors that operate against it are sand starvation, attack by transverse ridges, and encroachment by vegetation.

Neither pattern is found anywhere stabilized under forest. The characteristic forms are apparently gradually transformed into those determined by a plant cover in conjunction with wind and water.

SAND, WIND, WATER, AND VEGETATION: PHYTOGENIC DUNE DEVELOPMENT
ROLE OF PLANTS IN THE SYSTEM

Plants, except in the initial stage of invasion, do not ordinarily exert their influence as individuals but rather *en masse*, as communities. A community may be made up of individuals of the same species, but it is commonly more complex, including many species of diverse types. A forest, for example, includes trees, shrubs, and herbs, interacting to form a well-knit whole. There are many sorts of communities, and the resulting variety in vegetation promotes diversity in dune forms.

The characteristic role of vegetation in the system is stabilization. It is thus in direct opposition to wind, the prime agent for mobility. Water is also a stabilizing influence, but because of evaporation and drainage its direct effects are comparatively transitory. The influence of vegetation lasts far longer. Many woody plants of the Oregon-Washington dunes are long-lived—up to 500 years and more. Being living things they reproduce their kind; generation follows generation. There is constant invasion by new individuals from near-by areas.

Plants exert a direct stabilizing influence on sand in two ways. They protect the surface from attack by wind and bind the superficial layer by a network of roots and underground stems. A further, indirect effect, in our region, is the formation under forest of a compact concentration layer, the B horizon of a podzolic soil. Playing their part in this, plants actually modify the physical-chemical nature of the sand mass in its surface portion. The concentration layer becomes effective after destruction of the forest, when it may for a time resist erosion and temporarily set the level below which removal of sand cannot go. It does not, however, in this region attain the hardness possessed by the *Ortstein* of the German dunes or the *alios* of those of Gascony.

Stabilization by vegetation is accomplished very gradually. A scattering of "pioneers" initiates the process. Community succeeds community; each one prepares the way for the next and thereby causes its own elimination. Each takes a firmer hold on the substratum, so that disturbance of the surface becomes constantly more difficult. The generalized series in this region is from sand-binding grasses, rushes, and creeping shrubs, through thicket to pine or spruce forest, and finally to the "climax" community of western hemlock, western arbor vitae, and Douglas fir. When the climax stage has been reached, barring disturbance by fire or other factors, stabilization may for practical purposes be considered permanent.

In the extensive literature dealing with the coastal dunes of Europe, strong emphasis has very naturally been laid upon plants as agents in dune building. It has been frequently stated or implied that for coastal dunes they are essential. Solger (1910, p. 143) states that ". . . for the formation of dunes sand is necessary first, then wind which carries it landward, and plants to hold it." Braun (1911, p. 138–139) makes the law world-wide in its application: "A survey of the coasts of the earth shows us immediately that, where the deposit on the shore is wholly or in part of sand and where the climate permits plant growth, the formation of dunes takes place, in greater or lesser degree according to local conditions. The coastal dune is thus an accumulation of sand made with the help of vegetation by the wind. The necessary elements and forces for its building are a, the sand, b, the wind, c, the plants."

Van Dieren (1934) presents an all-embracing classification of dunes with an elaborate Latin terminology. His two major classes are "physical dune forms", mainly characteristic of deserts, and "organogenic dune forms", in the building of which plants are essential agents. "In our latitude [that of Holland] a dune comes into being only with the aid of homogeneous masses of vegetation, which, even in humified state, form a constituent of the natural dune." (p. 105)

Other authors who assert the necessity of plants for the building of coastal dunes are Sokolow (1894), Cholnoky (1902), Briquet (1923), Hartnack (1925), and Enquist (1932).

In particular, it has been quite generally held that as a first step in the development of a coastal dune system the sand must be bound just above the shore in a foredune ridge, in the building of which certain grasses are essential. Solger (1910), treating the dunes of the Baltic and North Seas, asserts (p. 141) that ". . . in all the diversity we must always hold firmly to the fact that every coastal dune originally came from a vegetated foredune."

The contention that plants are indispensable for the building of coastal dunes is not valid. It is sufficient to cite a single extreme instance of coastal dunes with no associated vegetation—the coast of southern Peru and northern Chile, one of the driest regions of the earth (Bowman, 1924; Johnson, 1930; Rich, 1942; H. T. U. Smith, 1954). These dunes, of course, in a strict sense are coastal only with respect to the source of their sand; the forms they take are typically those of the desert: barchans, systems of transverse ridges, etc. (Johnson, 1930, Fig. 77; Rich, 1942, Figs. 271, 274). Such might be dismissed as desert dunes, ignoring the origin of the sand, were it not that the same desert forms occur on certain coasts with humid climate and luxuriant vegetation, e.g., the coast of Oregon. It has been shown in previous sections that here there are systems of typical transverse ridges and forms equivalent to "longitudinal dunes", both of which are commonly considered desert types. Distinction between desert and coastal dunes is less fundamental than differentiation among dune forms on the basis of the agents that bring them into being. Sand and wind interacting produce certain forms, which are found both in deserts and on coasts. The same is true when the factor water is added; the forms do not differ much from those made by the first two elements interacting. When vegetation is added to the system, radical changes are wrought; the resulting forms again occur on coasts and in continental, mostly arid, interiors.

The reason why on the humid Oregon coast, and presumably on some others with similar climate, plants are absent from the system over wide areas lies in the paucity and comparative ineffectiveness of sand-binding species able to withstand the severe conditions near the shore.[26] It is wrong to assume that moist climate will necessarily produce effective sand binders. On the many coasts where effective sand binders do exist, a foredune ridge parallel to the shore commonly comes into being, which may remain as a permanent feature or in breaking up give rise to a multiplicity of secondary features. Such is the case with the dunes of European coasts. But why, in the absence of effective vegetation, should not sand and wind interact in normal fashion next to the sea as well as in deserts?

---

[26] The following botanical data are offered pertaining to potential sand-binding plants that occur on the Washington-Oregon coast. A small number of native species qualify to some extent, none of them being outstandingly effective. They may be divided into two classes: the hillock builders, which bring about precipitation of the sand, and the surface binders, which stabilize an accumulation after it has been formed.

Of the hillock builders, those of the grass type are the most effective precipitators of sand on account of their erect habit and densely clustered stems and leaves. Dune grass—*Elymus arenarius* L. var. *villosus* Mey. (*E. mollis* Trin.)—is the only species that plays a significant role on this coast, and it grows in abundance only on prograding shores where it is safe from violent wave attacks. It ranges southward to the Salinas River in Central California but is of little consequence beyond the vicinity of the Columbia River. Incidentally, Elymus is an important sand binder on the coasts of northern Europe. The only other grass-type species is *Carex macrocephala* Willd. (*C. anthericoides* Presl) (a sedge). It is abundant in Washington and northern Oregon but is not very effective in sand precipitation. Salt rush (*Juncus lescurii* Boland.) is an effective hillock builder, but it grows behind the strand on moist stable surfaces reduced to deflation base.

Another type of hillock builder is the plant with procumbent stems tending toward erectness at the growing tip. This gives rise to a low mound of sand rather than an abrupt hillock. The yellow sand verbena (*Abronia latifolia* Eschsch.) and two species of burweed (*Franseria bipinnatifida* Nutt. and *F. chamissonis* Less.) are common on the Washington and Oregon shores, but the mounds they build are too widely spaced to have much effect. This type becomes increasingly important southward and attains real effectiveness in southern California where *Abronia maritima* Nutt. builds authentic foredune ridges.

The principal surface binders are shore morning glory (*Convolvulus soldanella* L.), richly stoloniferous, and sand strawberry (*Fragaria chiloensis* (L.) Duch.), which covers the surface with a network of runners.

The native flora of the Washington-Oregon coast does not, except for dune grass in its preferred environment, provide agents adequate for the building of a substantial foredune. A recently introduced grass is, however, thoroughly adequate. This is marram grass (*Ammophila arenaria* (L.) Link, native to Europe, and its close eastern American relative *A. breviligulata* Fern.). Marram grass is the plant mainly responsible for the foredune so heavily emphasized in the European literature; it has been used there for centuries for dune fixation. It was first introduced to the Pacific coast at San Francisco in 1869 for the stabilization of the dune area now replaced by Golden Gate Park (Lamb, 1898), and was brought to the Coos Bay region about 1910. From the original plantings and from many more that have since been made it has spread naturally along the coast and has produced in many places a prominent foredune where none existed before (Pl. 13, fig. 3; Pl. 14, fig. 1). Comparison of aerophotos made in 1940 and 1953 shows marked increase in extent and density in 13 years. Such an apparently unimportant event, the introduction of an exotic grass, may thus in the course of decades or centuries change significantly the character of the whole dune complex.

Comparison between the coasts of Oregon and Peru-Chile emphasizes a general effect of vegetation on dune development: its inhibiting influence on inland penetration by sand masses originating at the shore. The Peruvian-Chilean coast is quite similar to that of Oregon with respect to wind regime (Bowman, 1916, p. 128–131). The dominant winds are southwest, south, and southeast, obliquely onshore or almost parallel to the coast. For the most part they have the character of a strong afternoon sea breeze which attains its greatest vigor in summer. Correspondence to the northwest to north summer sea breeze of the Oregon Coast is apparent. The Peruvian-Chilean coast differs radically from that of Oregon in its extreme aridity; precipitation occurs only at intervals of several to many years. Vegetation, accordingly, is almost absent. Inland advance of the coastal sands is unlimited. Surface wind currents passing over and beyond ridges already formed carry sand to leeward. This settles and accumulates in mounds that develop into advance-guard barchans which consolidate into new ridges (Johnson, 1930, Figs. 10, 77). According to Rich (1942, p. 220) ". . . the sand, which is entirely derived from the beach, travels inland at least 10 to 15 miles (16–24 km) over all obstacles in its path." It climbs the coastal mountains to considerable heights (at least 1000 m), maintaining typical dune forms on piedmont slopes but forming drifts that simulate snow banks in the hollows of rugged terrain (Johnson, 1930, Fig. 42; Rich, 1942, Figs. 272, 273; H. T. U. Smith, 1954).

On the coast of Oregon, inland advance of the dunes is opposed by tall, dense forest. The surface currents here lose velocity, and the sand is dropped at the forest edge. General advance is by a slow forward creep of the slipface, which becomes constantly slower as the dune becomes more massive and the slipface higher. Greatest inland penetration by the dunes of the Washington-Oregon coast is only 4.5 km.

Slope in itself, even rugged mountain terrain, does not seriously hinder advance of the sand. If, however, forest is present, adverse slope adds significantly to the difficulty imposed by the former. On the Coos Bay dune sheet in Oregon 60 per cent of the inner margin lies at the foot of the mountain front. At but one point does it climb a steep slope—to a height of only 80 m above tide. The remainder falls short of the inner edge of the terrace strip or has been blocked by water bodies. Were it not for vegetation—ultimately, the climate that makes it possible—the seaward face of the Oregon Coast Range would be drifted with sand as are the slopes of the coastal mountains in Peru and Chile.

DUNE DEVELOPMENT ON A PROGRADING SHORE

In a later section it will be shown that the shore north and south of the Columbia, particularly the former, has for some thousands of years been undergoing active progradation. Dune forms and processes in such a situation are extremely simple. The land is built out to seaward by formation of successive beach ridges. Each newly formed ridge relieves the next older from wave attack. The strand plants of the coast, inefficient where conditions are at all difficult, are here able to establish themselves in numbers sufficient to fix the ridge as a primary dune structure which, very properly, may be termed a foredune.[27] Dune grass (Elymus) has doubtless been by far

---

[27] The term has sometimes been used in a vague sense to denote any sort of dune structure parallel to the shore, even a complex system of secondary forms—which spoils its usefulness.

the most effective since it thrives under burial (McLaughlin and Brown, 1942). Most of the sand blowing inland is precipitated by it upon the ridge, which grows into a massive, straight embankment. Normal vegetational succession quickly brings establishment of forest.

Systems of beach-dune ridges like these occur in many parts of the world. For the north German coasts they have been described by Jentsch (1900), Solger (1910), Braun (1911), and others. They are frequently, though not necessarily, associated with the mouths and deltas of great rivers (*see* Rich, 1942, p. 44, 48, and Figures 50, 58, 59, 60) as in the case of the Columbia.

DUNE DEVELOPMENT ON A RETROGRADING SHORE

Method of presentation.—The above major heading, which will have to serve for the present discussion, is not completely satisfactory for the portion of the coast, extending from Tillamook Head, Oregon, to the California boundary, which it covers. It applies in that the major dune features of the present came into being in a period of retrogradation, now long past. It is, however, only partially applicable with respect to this coast for the last several thousand years—the period when active progradation was going on north of Tillamook Head. During the latter time, continuing to the present, this coast has been in a state of comparative stability, retrograding slightly at some places and times and prograding slightly in others. The landscape here is so complex and varied that it is difficult to disentangle the processes that go into its making. The only feasible course is to present a few common situations and in each case to trace the chain of events that starts with interaction of vegetation and the other three elements at the shore. It is assumed that no foredune is present—the normal situation for this coast before the advent of the white man.

Flat shore, no dunes, with and without abundant sand supply.—If no effective vegetation is present the sand, if in good supply, moves inland in transverse ridges. If the flat behind the beach is forested, the wind moving against it loses velocity, drops its load at the forest front, and produces a precipitation ridge parallel to the shore, one of the two characteristic forms developed by the four-phase system (Pl. 12, fig. 3). It will have an important place later in the discussion. Slow advance because of resistance due to the trees results in rapid increase in bulk. If sand supply continues abundant, the space over which the precipitation ridge has traveled becomes mantled with transverse ridges, which supply material to the main structure. If supply becomes meager the area behind the ridge is reduced to deflation base, the level below which removal cannot proceed under existing conditions. This is determined by one of several factors. The surface of the substratum sets the ultimate limit. Within the sand mantle itself, the B horizon of a podzolic soil may temporarily put a stop to denudation. The water table, however, is the most important determining factor; sand removal becomes increasingly difficult as it is approached until deflation ceases altogether.

Assuming that deflation base has been determined by the water table, the water of the soil now acts as a stabilizing agent and is itself a raw material for plant metabolism. Conditions are thus immediately favorable for invasion, especially for plants requiring abundant moisture, and the factor vegetation re-enters the system. Salt rush and coast willow (*Salix hookeriana* Benth.) are the most important early invaders.

The period of meager sand supply may be followed by a period of increasing supply. If invasion by plants is still in its early stages, the clumps of salt rush and willow give rise to precipitation hillocks which acquire tongue hills pendent to leeward. Neighboring units coalesce into larger tongues which advance with the summer wind. A characteristic pattern, which shows on aerophotos as a series of closely placed sharp-pointed tongues of sand contrasting with the dark vegetation over which they are moving, develops (Pl. 14, fig. 2, lower left; Pl. 19, fig. 2, center; Pl. 4, locality 26). If abundant sand supply continues, the low vegetation will be overwhelmed, and transverse ridges will supersede the tongue pattern.

If increase in sand supply is delayed for a sufficient length of time, forest will become established on the deflation plain, and the chain of events will be quite different. The seaward portion of the area is first to be denuded and therefore is first to acquire a forest cover. As denudation progresses inland the forest belt widens. Reaching the base of the windward slope of the precipitation ridge, it follows it inland. The precipitation ridge, cut off from source of supply by failure at the beach and growth of forest, continues its advance with diminishing vitality. A new forest margin at the seaward edge of the deflation plain is ready, whenever sand supply becomes abundant, to bring about formation of a new precipitation ridge.

Stabilized dune masses undergoing erosion.—There are two subcases here, depending on whether the eroding mass is very thick or comparatively thin. The first may be quickly disposed of. Attrition of a thick dune mass is very slow, and the sole effective agent is the surf, the erosive action of which is confined to a narrow zone at the base of the bluff. Wind is extremely ineffective. The forest cover at the top disintegrates, and fragments slide to the beach. If pressure of the surf is relieved for a time, vegetation quickly takes hold upon the bluff; it acquires a forest cover in which pine ordinarily predominates. Lofty eroded dunes are at the present for the most part in a state of partial or complete stabilization. Noteworthy examples occur in Localities 5, 7, 8, 21, and 22. The last is shown in Figure 3 of Plate 18. Where the substratum is above sea level, the sea in its advance will in time cut into it. "Perched" dunes are the result, and these, in spite of their exposed position, maintain their original forms with great persistence (Localities 10, 15, 18, and many minor occurrences).

In the second subcase the older stabilized dunes do not stand high above the sea. Surf is the agent that initiates activity, but wind takes over immediately, and the resulting events are complex. The situation is best exemplified in Locality 19, where a rather thin dune sheet of moderate relief completely covers a low terrace 4.5 km wide, slightly below tide at the shore. Stabilized dune masses extend in places to the beach. There is here ample space for development of varied forms. All features of importance appear in the vertical aerial view (Pl. 14, fig. 2).

TROUGH BLOWOUT: In the vicinity of Heceta Beach at the edge of the stabilized dune sheet is a low cliff cut by waves in the dune mass. Resisting power along the cliff is not everywhere the same. At vulnerable spots the wind effects a break, and a trough blowout is initiated (Pl. 14, fig. 2, lower right; Pl. 14, fig. 3). The re-entrant causes convergence of current threads and thus local increase in velocity, which brings increased power for erosion and transportation. The trough is cut constantly farther back in line with the direction of the effective wind. When an appreciable length has been attained, the drag due to the walls and the vegetation surmounting them retards the velocity along the sides, and the marginal portion of the current is laterally deflected. Air moving over the sides loses velocity very rapidly, principally because of the vegetation; it drops its load of sand almost immediately and produces an incipient precipitation ridge. As this grows in height it increases resistance to air movement, and it may itself become partially stabilized by plants of the pioneer type.

The central stream, essentially maintaining its velocity, continues headward erosion. Here, too, sand is piled into the forest ahead of it, but the force is sufficient to keep it moving and to prevent stabilization. The trees are first partially buried, and as erosion progresses they are undermined. Rapidity of headward erosion depends primarily upon the bulk of sand encountered. Deep deposits will hinder, shallow deposits hasten the process. Type of forest also has an effect: pine is easily destroyed, spruce is more resistant.

The bottom of the trough is ordinarily not swept clear. Masses of sand derived from erosion of the side walls and from the beach move inland (Pl. 14, fig. 3). The surfaces of most of these are irregular because of the confused turbulence of the air, but in troughs that are relatively broad there may be a rough approximation to transverse ridges.

MERGING OF TROUGHS AND REDUCTION TO DEFLATION BASE: In spite of reduced velocity of the laterally deflected currents and resistance offered by forest and precipitation ridges, erosion of the sides makes constant progress, and the trough is thereby widened. The sides of two adjacent troughs approach each other; their lateral precipitation ridges finally merge into an intertrough ridge. Recession of the sides is variable because of differences in depth of sand and in type of tree encountered. Shallow burial alone is fatal to pine; encroachment on pine forest is relatively rapid. Spruces thrive under burial and send out massive roots into the sand with remarkable rapidity. They become more resistant rather than less. The sides of adjacent troughs may thus approach each other more rapidly at some points than at others, and in time the intertrough ridge is cut through completely and broken into segments parallel in alignment to the troughs. These are gradually reduced until all that remains is a row of knobs, each one commonly held by a group of spruces (Pl. 14, fig. 2, bottom foreground; Pl. 7, fig. 2). The pattern developed during reduction of the forested masses is not always so systematic. Bare areas of irregular shape, which increase in size and in time coalesce, are opened up. With disappearance of the last remnants the landscape is converted into a plain covered with mobile sand, and here the sequence of events merges with that originating on a flat shore destitute of older dunes, already described.

FURTHER HISTORY OF THE PRECIPITATION RIDGE: With elimination of the intertrough masses, the advancing dune front, at first extremely irregular, is gradually transformed into a massive, continuous precipitation ridge (Pl. 14, fig. 2; Pl. 15, fig. 1). Its profile is similar to that of the ordinary transverse ridge, with a gentle windward slope and a typical slipface. The mode of advance is also similar: sand removed from the windward slope is carried over the top and falls on the slipface. Its mass in full development is, however, much greater than that of any transverse ridge. Its advancing front may equal or even overtop the forest standing in its way. Height of the crest varies from place to place. Where activity is most pronounced, bulges project to leeward. The windward slope often bears transverse ridges that may be traced back in a general way to those that originated on the denuded area and overtook the precipitation ridge in its slower progress.

The precipitation ridge in its advance commonly brings total destruction by burial to the vegetation in its path (Pl. 15, fig. 2). Pine is quickly killed. Douglas fir may survive if enough of its top protrudes from the sand. Spruce and Port Orford cedar, through production of adventitious roots, are best able to withstand burial. As the ridge moves on, dead trunks and a few trees with living tops emerge from the windward slope (Pl. 15, fig. 3; Pl. 20, fig. 2). As long as a supply of mobile sand is available the ridge increases in mass. When vegetation has captured the deflated area to windward, sand supply is entirely cut off (Pl. 15, fig. 1). There is no further increase; henceforth advance is a matter of turnover of the materials contained in the ridge itself.[28] There will even be some slight decrease because of sand carried away by high winds and by attrition of particle on particle. The ridge increases in height at the expense of its breadth, because shift of the windward margin, where removal of loose sand is easy, is more rapid than advance of the leeward edge, which is due to slow forward creep of the slipface. At one point in Locality 19 the slipface made an average annual advance of 1.02 m in 6 years (Table 8). On the windward side of the same ridge, directly opposite, determination of tree ages along a line perpendicular to the axis of the ridge gave a consistent gradient from 5 years near the windward edge of the ridge to 65 years at a point 154 m to seaward. The rate of forest advance thus indicated is 2.57 m per year. Since trees establish themselves as soon as the requisite conditions of stability and moisture are provided, their advance furnishes a rough measure of leeward shift of the margin of the moving sand. It is not implied that the difference in rate is always as great as in this case.

Invading vegetation reaching the base of the windward slope of the ridge does not stop there but continues its advance. Forest to windward shelters the lowermost portion of the slope and decreases sand movement. Pioneer plants—lichens, mosses, grasses, trailing shrubs, and brush—creep upward and are followed by the forest. More sand is anchored; less goes over the top, and this is distributed over an increasing area of slipface as the ridge grows in height. As vegetation advances irregularly toward the top of the windward slope, the remaining bare area is broken into fragments, which dwindle until pine forest and ultimately the climax covers all. The slipface itself becomes more stable and gradually acquires a cover of vegetation consisting of plants rooted in the substratum and able to keep pace with sand accumulation and others germinating on the surface. Movement is at an end. Although the ridge is now completely fixed, the term, precipitation ridge, indicating its origin, may be retained. In contrast to forms related to the system sand, wind, water, without vegetation, the precipitation ridge is preserved in its final form under a forest cover.

Stabilization of the windward slope is subject to fluctuations and minor setbacks. Areas in the lichen, grass, and shrub stages, fairly stable in general but having spots thinly vegetated or bare, are susceptible to renewal of erosion. Because of the constantly changing contour of near-by ridges and forests, surface air currents are

---

[28] Such a ridge is closely comparable with the Wanderdüne of German authors.

erratic. Concentration on a vulnerable spot causes local sand removal; a saucer blowout[29] is initiated. Adjacent areas with denser vegetation are resistant. The hollow is enlarged by undermining, producing relatively steep sides, and the more resistant the surface the steeper are the slopes. Turbulence within the hollow increases effectiveness of the wind. A portion of the sand removed is scattered widely but most is piled just beyond the edge, especially along the southeast sector (the leeward side in summer).[30] The active life of a saucer blowout may be very brief, or neighboring ones may enlarge and coalesce, giving greater sweep to the wind although decreasing the concentrated effect of turbulence. A second saucer may develop within a partially stabilized older one, and the resulting topography may thus become very complex in detail (Pl. 15, fig. 4). The surface of the windward slope after complete stabilization is hummocky, retaining distinct traces of the saucer blowouts and piles of sand derived from them. The lee slope remains relatively smooth; it may become steepened beyond the angle of repose through retention of sliding sand by vegetation.

The opposing forces underlying erosion and stabilization are in delicate balance. A change in wind or precipitation or uneven development of the protective forest may initiate a trend in either direction. In particular, a series of wet years will hasten the process of stabilization, and a prolonged relatively dry period will cause increase in area dominated by mobile sand. If the effects of the drier periods equal or surpass those of the wetter, a condition of incomplete stabilization may persist for a long time. Barring catastrophic events—fire in particular—the general advance of vegetation goes on inexorably. As the open areas dwindle and protection by forest increases in effectiveness, the chance of local erosion becomes constantly less until finally it vanishes.

REJUVENATION OF THE PRECIPITATION RIDGE: The minor setbacks just described may fairly be considered as rejuvenation on a small scale. Sometimes, due to certain agencies that operate with special potency, destruction spreads until the whole ridge becomes mobile, even though it may have reached an advanced stage in the process of stabilization. Four agencies are conceivably competent to initiate rejuvenation on a major scale: drought, lumbering, windthrow, and fire. Under the extremely humid climate of this coast droughts of sufficient intensity to destroy or damage seriously a completely closed vegetation cover do not occur. Periods of relatively low precipitation are effective only in temporarily increasing erosional activity in areas not completely stabilized. The lumbering era extends back only a few decades, and very little timber has been cut from the dunes. On the largest clear-cut area (Locality 24) there has been a small amount of reactivation of the sand, but for the most part the floor of the former forest is intact. Windthrow is frequent in the coastal forests, but there is no evidence that it is an important factor in causing rejuvenation on the dunes. Fire is adequate as a cause, and there is abundant evidence that it has been effective. Many buried soil horizons have burned stumps and logs, or at least charred wood, associated with them. The present forest on the dunes, especially north of the Siuslaw River, is predominantly of even-aged lodgepole pine—the fire tree of the coastal

[29] German: *Windmulde*; French: *caoudeyre*.
[30] German: *Haldendüne*.

region—and there are numerous remains of a preceding generation killed by fire. Before the advent of *Homo sapiens*, fires must have been due to lightning, which is infrequent on the coast in summer. With the coming of the aborigines fires became more frequent. The European whites caused an epidemic of fires in the region, but the dunes have been little affected by these.

Fire in this region rarely initiates rejuvenation by direct action, *i.e.*, by stripping completely the vegetal cover and the surface soil made resistant by its effects. The geological effects of a forest fire, moreover, are confined to masses of sand lying above the general water table. Renewal of sand movement is therefore restricted mainly to ridgy masses, and rejuvenation is set in motion by destruction of the protecting forest surrounding areas where the surface is still vulnerable, giving access to the surface air currents. Saucer blowouts form in such places; they enlarge rapidly and coalesce. Areas forested before the fire are undermined, and finally the entire windward slope loses its vegetation cover. Sand is carried over the stabilized lee slope, at first locally, eventually resulting in the formation of a continuous slipface. The trees on the lee slope are partly or wholly buried and later undermined. The factor vegetation has again been eliminated. The other three interact, even to the extent that a system of transverse ridges is produced on the windward slope. The precipitation ridge has been reconstituted as a mobile unit.

Although a completely stabilized ridge is almost immune to direct rejuvenation, it can easily be destroyed by attack from without. If such a mass lies to leeward of a ridge that has undergone complete rejuvenation, the slipface of the latter may invade it and finally pass over the top. The materials of the older ridge are added to the younger, increasing its mass and length of life.

Repeated fires at relatively short intervals maintain the rejuvenated ridge in a state of mobility. Assuming freedom from fire for a sufficiently long period, the normal processes of plant colonization reassert themselves, the mobile areas are gradually restricted, and complete stabilization is reattained.

PARABOLA DUNE: The second distinctive form in the building of which vegetation plays a part is the parabola dune.[31] It is essentially a trough blowout of major size with massive terminal and lateral walls, which because of its bulk has attained a state of quasi-permanence. Three conditions are prerequisite for its development: (1) A generally stabilized surface, essential for concentration of effective attack by wind at a point of weakness. (2) Considerable initial thickness of sand. If the layer of potentially mobile sand beneath the stabilized surface is thin, adjacent troughs will quickly widen and coalesce, concentration of attack will be lost, and advance will henceforth take place on a wide front. (3) Unidirectional effective wind. If both summer and winter winds come to bear, incipient troughs will intersect and tend to cancel each other. With unidirectional wind the trough will extend itself free from interference. The first two of these conditions are provided in many places. The third is the critical one. Essentially unidirectional wind occurs where local topographic

---

[31] This term, in common use by German authors (Parabeldüne), is misleading in its implication of strict mathematical form, but is so firmly established in the literature that its continued acceptance seems reasonable. H. T. U. Smith (1945–46) has suggested the term "upsiloidal."

features reduce the effectiveness of either winter or summer wind to a point so low that the other is in almost complete control. It happens that, in places otherwise favorable for building of parabolas, protection from summer wind is by far the commoner case. Hence most of the parabola dunes, under the influence of south to southwest winds, develop northward to northeastward. Once firmly established, a parabola dune may rise above its protecting feature and continue to grow in size. Like the precipitation ridge, it retains its characteristic form after complete stabilization by forest.

Satisfactory ground photography of parabola dunes is impossible. Aerophotos, however, portray them well. The mosaic (Pl. 16, Locality 9) shows the largest of the single parabola dunes.

In its development from a blowout, the older, windward portion of the trough deepens and broadens, and its marginal ridges are gradually cut away. In the younger leeward portion, headward and lateral piling up continues. The axial profile of the structure consists of a gradually ascending windward slope and a normal slipface beyond the apex, which is in most cases the highest point of the whole. Where sand supply is abundant, transverse ridges may travel up the trough.

Continued maintenance of activity depends upon a continued supply of fresh sand, either directly from the shore or from an extensive area of rejuvenation. If the supply is cut off, stabilization proceeds rapidly. During the process activity is frequently renewed in local spill-overs at various points around the apex and along the side walls, and the sand slides down the outer slope, sometimes even to the base, destroying the vegetation upon it. These spillovers gradually become quiescent; in the meantime activity is initiated at other points. Symmetry of the mass as a whole is not seriously disturbed by such sporadic outbreaks. The portion that retains activity longest is a strip along the axis of the trough. If sand supply is renewed, rejuvenation occurs, first along the axis, gradually spreading until sand once more spills over the outer slopes.

It sometimes happens that, due to temporary decrease of activity, the floor of the trough becomes partially stabilized. In such a case a new blowout trough may form; a new parabola dune has been initiated, nested within the older. Partial stabilization may again take place, and a third trough and parabola may be formed.

In a favorable situation several parabola structures may develop side by side, sometimes so close that the spaces between them are sharp ravines; a parabola complex is thus produced. Figure 1 of Plate 18 and Figure 1 of Plate 19 include parabola complexes; Figure 2 of Plate 18 is an oblique view of the complex of Figure 1 of Plate 18. The windward-pointing extremities of the massive intertrough ridges, fully exposed to the erosive action of the wind, recede, and the sand thus released is swept into and up the troughs on either side. The whole parabola complex thus moves inland, leaving behind it an ever-increasing area of open sand. If wasting of the intertrough "peninsulas" exceeds advance of the parabola apices, the peninsulas must become constantly shorter and finally be eliminated. A bow-shaped precipitation ridge will then replace the group of parabola dunes.

The massiveness of the Oregon parabola dunes is due to the height of the forest barrier and its resistance to destruction, and ultimately, therefore, to the climate. On the coast of middle and southern California, where thinner vegetation makes a far less effective obstacle, the parabola is the dominating form in the major dune fields. The units are closely placed, even overlapping. They are not massive, but are sometimes very long. Their life span, moreover, is short compared with those of the Oregon coast.

PART III: THE DUNES OF THE OREGON-WASHINGTON COAST

FOUR DUNE REGIONS

Tillamook Head, 32 km south of the Columbia River, is a primary point of division on the coast between two completely dissimilar dune landscapes. The transition is abrupt; there are no localities intermediate in character. North of this point the dunes make a continuous strip broken only by river and bay mouths and by a single headland. The forms are the simple ones characteristic of a prograding shore: systems of regular ridges parallel to the beach. They have been little disturbed. South of the Head this type is absent; the dunes are strictly localized, and their forms are heterogeneous and complex.

The group of four localities north of Tillamook Head is designated Region I. For adequate treatment of the southern localities subdivision is necessary, and Regions II, III, and IV are recognized. These are considered first, since Region I is a rather special case.

REGION II: NORTHERN OREGON
GENERAL FEATURES

Region II comprises 14 localities lying between Tillamook Head and Heceta Head, a distance of 200 km. The coast is rocky; only 53 km, or 27 per cent of the whole, bears dunes. Of the 14 localities, 10 contribute significantly to our knowledge of the general history, and their features are shown in the tracings from mosaics presented in Plate 2.[32] Eight localities are related to river or bay mouths. All but one of these (Locality 14) are alike in having as principal feature a parabola or parabola complex or a remnant thereof at the north end resting upon a terrace substratum or ascending the mountain slope. A secondary feature in most is a line of remnant forested dunes upon a peninsula outside the river mouth or bay and roughly continuing southward the eastern margin of the parabola complex. These represent the southern portion of the dune mass, most of which has been cut away by the sea. In some localities cutting has gone faster or more continuously than in others. In extreme cases the remnants of the system—the parabola complex and the southward-extending marginal ridge or its fragments—are so isolated from each other that ground study alone fails to show their close relationship. Aerial photographs reveal the common pattern.

The eight localities are arranged in a series based upon approximate order in degree of truncation. For locations on the coast *see* Plate 1.

LOCALITY 9: SAND LAKE

"Sand Lake" is a misnomer. The feature is in no sense a lake, but rather an area of tidal flats, of shifting sands and channels, having salt marsh along the edges, and occupying the lowest part of an indentation in the upland.

---

[32] Absolute accuracy in delineation of topographic expression by tracing aerophotos is impossible, principally because of the dense forest that mantles the stabilized dune masses, and it is manifestly impracticable to check every feature on the ground. Uncertainty with respect to significant features is indicated by a question mark.

The main portion of the dune mass is a single parabola of enormous size, 4.5 km long, 1–1.5 km wide (Pl. 16). For the purpose of correlation with similar structures to be later described, the process of its building is designated Episode I. Its axis is oriented approximately N. 30° E. Its rearward portion has been sliced cleanly away by the advancing sea on a line trending approximately southward. Here the dune sand crowns a steep bluff which from its first appearance at *A* increases northward in height to a maximum of 50 m at point *B*, where the margin of the dune mass swings inland. The altitude of the substratum at the northern tip of the parabola, approximately at the foot of the mountain slope, is almost 100 m.

The main body is stabilized and densely forested. Its outer margins take the form of ridges steep-sided within as well as without, since erosion played a large part in forming their inner slopes. Inside the marginal ridges are old deflation surfaces and an inner parabola (Episode II), hairpin-shaped and, like the outer, broken through at the tip. It too has a deflation surface within its walls. Obviously, in reconstructing its original state, the parabola must be projected south-southwestward a considerable distance beyond the present shore line.

South of the principal dune system are two areas of low stabilized dunes (*C*, *D*) that seem originally to have formed a salient in the inner marginal ridge of the main complex. One of these stands now upon an island between the two tidal channels.[33] The other shows parabola forms on a very small scale built by the summer wind.

Present activity is manifest in a strip of mobile sand lying along the axis of the main parabola from the shore to its tip. It comprises four units, each with a high active slipface. The terminal, oldest unit is almost as broad as long, and its area is more than 1 square km. The sand in its advance has flowed over the final stabilized precipitation ridge both at the apex and along the southeast flank and reaches ground never before invaded by dunes. The next two younger units are narrow; the youngest is again broad and opens out to the short, broad spit, which has been entirely denuded.

The small stabilized area on the island is being invaded by a low active precipitation ridge, the mass south of the outlet by trough blowouts oriented with the summer wind. Remnants indicate that the latter mass recently extended farther southward.

LOCALITY 5: NEHALEM RIVER

The system consists of a parabola complex at the north end and an almost denuded spit projecting southward outside the lower course of the Nehalem River. The substratum for the northern half of the parabola complex is of terrace nature, barely above sea level at the shore, 30–50 m above tide at the inner margin. There is no sea cliff. The southern half of the complex is adjacent to tidal flats on the east, and the substratum is below sea level on the west.

The seaward portion of the complex has been shorn away by the advancing sea. The mass that remains gives evidence of two major periods of activity preceding the present one, each followed by thorough stabilization. The earliest period of activity, Episode I (I, Pl. 2, Locality 5), produced a precipitation ridge with a steep lee slope and a long gentle windward slope, and behind this a wide deflation area reduced

---

[33] The Tillamook Quadrangle map of the U. S. Geological Survey is in error; the island is not shown.

almost to the substratum surface. The second period of activity (Episode II) gave rise to a second precipitation ridge, strongly lobate, which suggests merging of adjacent parabola structures. Toward the shore this ridge invaded the deflation area of Episode I; eastward it is very massive and extends into territory not previously invaded. Behind precipitation ridge II are the usual deflation area and recessional ridges, including an elongated parabola and a smaller one nested within it.

As in Locality 9, reconstruction of the dune mass in its early state necessitates projection south-southwestward beyond the present shore line. Its inner marginal ridge survives under severe attack as far as the bend in the river. The structures that occupied the present deflation area and the spit have been swept completely away.

Sand is invading the stabilized masses on three sectors (Episode III). Next to the shore trough blowouts and sand tongues penetrate the forest margin; progress is slow, and a continuous slipface is not established. Invasion of the inner marginal ridge next to the river is also slow. Sand from the shore, augmented by material eroded from the ridge itself, flows up and over the crest, and descends the lee slope on narrow slipfaces. The ridge is cut into fragments which will dwindle and disappear. The middle sector is by far the most active. It lies broadside to the winter winds, and much of the sand carried into the deflation area by the summer wind is later deflected northeastward. A massive precipitation ridge has developed which is advancing on a broad front, overtopping the forest in its path. If this sector were to be stabilized and forested in its present state it would become a replica of precipitation ridge I.

LOCALITY 10: NESTUCCA BAY

Nestucca Bay is hardly more than an estuary at the mouth of a river of moderate size. It enters the ocean at the south end of a long spit which at one point is almost cut through by a meander. There is an extensive parabola complex at the north, and the spit bears remnant masses.

There is also a feature difficult to understand without reference to the historical factor: a group of isolated remnants of dune sand—the largest 25 m thick, showing six soil horizons in its eroding flanks and still bearing forest—resting upon the summit of Cape Kiwanda (A, Pl. 2, Locality 10; Pl. 17, fig. 1). In the earlier part of the period of submergence there stood here a prominent headland. The surviving remnants are Haystack Rock, an isolated protuberance of volcanic material rising 100 m above present sea level, and Cape Kiwanda, of weaker, sedimentary rock but directly in the lee of Haystack with respect to the violent storms of winter. Cape Kiwanda, incidentally, is not simply a terrace remnant, since it rises at least 30 m above the rock platform just north of the cape, which stands at about 10 m (Snavely, 1948).

In the lastest major advance of the sea Haystack Rock acted as a bastion of resistance protecting the weaker materials behind it. The shore, maintaining its connection with the Rock, receded on both sides of it, more rapidly on the south because of exposure to the winter storms. The resulting concavity south of the headland, bringing the shore line into a position broadside to waves and wind, became a favorable lodgment area for sand. The oldest parabola unit of which there is evidence had its inception under these conditions. The sand moved north-northeastward just inside Haystack Rock, up and over the hill that is now Cape Kiwanda, and along the terrace surface east of it. Stabilization and development of a forest cover followed. The life of this first unit was a comparatively brief one, for the sea continued its cutting, both north and south of Haystack Rock. The peninsula became constantly narrower and was finally broken through, and the Rock was made an island. The parabola lost its source of supply and was beheaded as well. The remnants of dune sand surmounting the shrunken cape testify to the considerable bulk of the original mass.

The remainder of the dune complex consists of three contiguous parabolas, successively shorter eastward. They rest upon terrace at the north, and at the south, where the shifting course of the Nestucca River has cut away the terrace, on alluvium. They touch the base of the mountain front on the east, and here three lakes have formed in blocked ravines. All three parabolas have undergone rejuvenation along their axes, and each active strip has a second wave of advancing sand.

In the western of the three parabolas recent activity has been superficial and consists of a shallow flow of sand up and over the older stabilized ridges. It is now on the wane, and the slipfaces are in the early stages of stabilization. The second and third parabolas, though shorter, are higher than the first; the altitude of the easternmost ridge where it rests on alluvium is not much less than 100 m. The slipfaces, though not extensive, are high and active.

Within the bend of the Nestucca River and separated from the main mass by it are dune ridges of weak expression, reminiscent of the island area at the mouth of Sand Lake. The spit is mainly flat and bare. Low forested remnants occur along its inner edge, undergoing invasion by sand tongues. Two rather large barchanlike masses standing farther out embody the materials of older stabilized dunes now converted to complete mobility. Their slipfaces face northward, and in time they will move into the river and disappear.

At the maximum of submergence the shore line between Cape Kiwanda and the mouth of the Nestucca seems to have differed somewhat from the present. The spit was shorter and did not stand as far to seaward. The sea cliffs south of the river mouth, now protected, were open to attack by the surf (*see* Locality 11, following).

The course of the Nestucca River behind the spit has not remained constant. In its shiftings, the details of which are obscure, it has sliced off a portion of the innermost parabola ridge and cut off the area of weak dune ridges at Pacific City from the shore.

LOCALITY 11: NESKOWIN CREEK

Locality 11 does not belong in the series based on degree of truncation but is treated here because of its close relationship to Locality 10. The significant feature is a beach-dune barrier that lies partly in contact with the cliffed mountain front and partly in advance of it; it cuts off two prominent re-entrants. The cliffs were cut at the maximum of the last major submergence. Although for the most part they are now immune to wave attack, they are similar in every respect to those directly exposed, *e.g.*, along Cascade Head just south, except that they are for the most part clothed with vegetation, including trees of considerable size. At the north end of the locality the cliffs extend inland along the shore of Nestucca Bay for about 1 km, indicating penetration by the sea at its high stand to the point where they end.

The sea at its farthest advance did not everywhere reach the mountain front. Protruding masses were bevelled and the tips of promontories cut off. At one point, Daley Lake, a re-entrant was penetrated and a cliff cut along its inner shore. A deeper and more extensive re-entrant farther south acquired protection by a bay bar whose course seems to be marked by three small areas of higher ground, indicated by forest in the midst of bog (*A*, Pl. 2, Locality 11). It may well have been buttressed by a prominent isolated rock mass with cliffed outer face (*B*). Behind this bar a shallow lagoon developed in which peat has accumulated undisturbed to the present.

The heavy dot-dash lines in Plate 2, Locality 11, representing the positions of bay bars, and the cliffed segments connected by them, indicate the approximate position of the shore line at maximum of submergence.

Cliffing of the mountain front was followed by progradation, which may have produced a succession of regular beach ridges like those of the localities of Region I, but certainly on a much smaller scale. Renewed attack by the sea converted the primary accumulations into a strip made up of secondary forms—trough blowouts, small parabolas. These masses were driven shoreward and finally, with slackening wave attack, were stabilized and forested. The new barrier thus formed brought Daley Lake into existence and added much to the area of peat accumulation in the re-entrant farther south.

The present phase is one of destruction. The strip of stabilized dunes, never great in mass, has so wasted away that only a thin, much broken line remains. Wind erosion and burial by wind-blown sand have been constantly in operation; in addition there has been direct attack by waves during winter storms (which is taken as a matter of course by the local residents, in spite of considerable property damage—R. L. Brown, personal communication). The effects are plainly evident on aerophotos taken in the spring of 1939. The surf had poured through a number of gaps in the thin defensive line and flooded the low ground to the rear, laying down "washover fans" (Price 1947, p. 1653) where the overflows occurred (*C*, Pl. 2, Locality 11).

The sequence of events as outlined is the minimum required to account for the features of today. Greater complexity is probable; the cycle of stabilization and destruction may have been repeated several times.

LOCALITY 16: ALSEA BAY

"Alsea Bay" (Pl. 2, Locality 16) is another estuary at the mouth of a river of average Coast Range size, with outlet south of a short, blunt spit bare of dunes. The narrow parabola complex stands upon a low terrace; small lakes fill shallow depressions in the surface behind the dunes. The principal features are two elongated parabolas. Sliced-off remnants farther north probably represent one or more others. The dunes are not high; they attain a maximum altitude of about 35 m above tide. Vigorous rejuvenation of the two parabolas is now in progress in the form of an inward surge of activity along their axes. At the apices are slipfaces advancing so rapidly that the tops of still-living trees project a considerable distance behind them. Farther down the troughs, where the climax of the surge has passed, the lateral ridges are partially stabilized both on the inner eroded slopes and the former slip-faces outside.

LOCALITY 15: YAQUINA BAY

Although the dune masses at Yaquina Bay (Pl. 2, Locality 15) obviously belong to the same series as those previously described, certain differences appear which will recur in the next two localities. In the first four the river or bay mouth is at the south end of the dune mass or close to it; there are areas of active rejuvenation, and connection has been maintained between these and the shore. In the present and the next two the mouth is near the north end of the system; the parabola complex at the north end, reduced to a mere remnant, is cut off from its former source of supply and is completely inactive.

At Yaquina Bay the surviving fragment of the parabola complex stands upon a terrace peninsula bounded on three sides by bluffs. Thickness of dune sand is not great, and the original pattern is difficult to determine. Ridges, steep on both flanks, various in orientation, alternate with flat areas, apparently deflation surfaces. Since the highest ridges are along the northeast margin, it is probable that the original source of supply was in the southwest.

The southern member of the system, which here is south of the bay mouth, rests upon a low foreland more than 1 km wide. The bay outlet originally flowed south-westward along the base of the curving bluff; a portion of the old channel depression still survives near the bay, and several small ponds probably indicate its further course. The outlet shifted northward, cut away the terrace upon which stand the dunes of the parabola complex, and deprived them of their source of supply. It left behind it an alluvial flat, and over this successive waves of sand moved southeastward propelled by the summer winds. Precipitation ridge I, though indefinite in places and nowhere attaining an altitude of 15 m, is unequivocal. Ridge II is more pronounced and has many points over 15 m and a considerable mass at the north end. Ridge III is the product of the present phase of activity. Should stabilization of this ridge take place, a replica of the two preceding would result.

With each advancing wave the area behind the precipitation ridge was left almost bare, stripped to deflation base. The deflated areas behind ridges I and II are very flat and stand only 5 m above sea level. That related to I has, in addition to quasi-climax forest, large areas of peat. The deflation area associated with II is densely forested with pine. A new deflation area, similar to the older ones in every respect except its lack of vegetation, is developing behind the present active ridge.

LOCALITY 8: NETARTS BAY

Locality 8 (Pl. 2) is a counterpart of its neighbor Sand Lake so far as the general situation is concerned, as it is a re-entrant in the coast line containing a very shallow bay that receives no drainage other than that from short intermittent streams.

The parabola complex is represented by truncated extremities of three once massive parabolas. It is plain that their development—their final stabilization, in fact—must have taken place while the shore line was a considerable distance west of its present position. Beneath the seaward edge of Parabola A there is visible, where not concealed by slumping sand, a cliff about 15 m high. The truncated face of the dune, in part firmly stabilized by forest, rises 35 m above it. From this line the dune mass ascends the mountain slope and attains a substratum altitude of at least 120 m in a horizontal distance of 900 m. Within the parabola are the tips of two "recessional" structures. Parabola B, whose cut-off face is densely forested, climbs the mountain slope to a height of 60 m. Parabola C, also with a forested cut face, rests upon a low, flat terrace and therefore, though as massive as the others, does not attain so great an altitude.

Netarts Bay is separated from the ocean by a spit 6 km long. For most of its length it bears a narrow strip of dunes which, projected north-northeastward, leads to the parabola remnant C. This clearly represents the inner marginal portion of an extensive dune mass of which the parabola complex is the apex, and most of which has been cut away. The dunes upon it are all low; no summit attains an altitude greater than 15 m. At one point there is a remnant of a stabilized marginal ridge (D) with a steep forested slope facing the bay. A little farther south are two ridges parallel to it which project upon the marshy flat that borders the bay (E). They seem to sink beneath the floor, and this suggests that their bases have been buried by sediments laid down by tidal currents at a slightly higher stand of sea level.

The small features in the dune strip caused by wind erosion are related entirely to the northwest winds of summer. At the north end rapid destruction goes on. Small tree-crowned remnants and a single mass of sand converted to full mobility persist.

At the southern end of the spit the dune strip has been cut completely through; all that remains is a barrier beach between bay and ocean with some fast-eroding remnants upon it. In recent years storms have broken across this barrier; waves and wind have carried sand from the ocean into the bay (F). The pattern made by these deposits, superposed upon the normal pattern of shoals and tidal channels and plainly visible from the air, is indicated on the tracing. Most of this destruction was wrought by two exceptional storms in 1939, the effects of which here and on neighboring parts of the coast will be described in connection with Locality 7.

Netarts Bay, like its neighbor Sand Lake, in view of its scanty inflow, could very well have gotten along without a permanent outlet. If it had such it must have been at the far south end; otherwise there would have been no source of supply for the building of the parabola complex at the north. The water body may even have been for a time a fresh-water lake, slightly above sea level, with a feeble outlet, perhaps discharging by seepage during much of the year.

As the sea advanced, the dune masses standing at a low level were destroyed by waves and wind—all but the remnants that persist upon the spit. In its attack upon the northern complex, however, the sea encountered the resistant substratum; the dunes resting upon it have survived. Since height of the substratum increases rapidly inland, the rate of further destruction will constantly decrease.

The break-through which gave rise to the present outlet came late in the history, for the parabola complex was fully formed and completely stabilized when it occurred. Its cause may well have been a severe storm, or more likely a series of them, which cut through the dune barrier at a point of weakness. The bare north end of the spit must have been formed subsequently, since effective wave attack on parabola remnants B and C would require full exposure to surf from the southwest. Once well established, the outlet has been maintained by tidal currents and outflow contributed by streams during the season of heavy rains. The old outlet at the south, if such existed, was quickly closed by the building of a barrier ridge, and it is quite possible that the very narrow portion of the spit where surf has recently broken over is actually this ridge shifted inland. Present destruction at this point is unlikely to result in another shift of outlet as the existing one is firmly established.

LOCALITY 7: TILLAMOOK BAY

In general there is here close resemblance to Netarts Bay, the next locality south. The principal difference is that Tillamook Bay receives the waters of several streams having a combined drainage area of considerable size—which, however, seems not to have had an appreciable influence on the history of the dunes.

The parabola complex (Pl. 2, Locality 7) is represented by a single short massive ridge just north of the bay outlet and adjacent to the pre-jetty shore line. Its position relative to the complete dune system of the locality as reconstructed is the same as if, at Netarts Bay, all had been cut away except a narrow slice at the apex of parabola A. According to the Geological Map of Northwestern Oregon (U. S. Geological Survey, 1945) the substratum is a small detached block of Tertiary shale, presumably a low terrace surface. The ridge rises 75 m above sea level, and nearly all this thickness must be dune sand. The landward face is a compound terminal lee slope, the seaward, one of truncation. Half of the latter is densely forested; the other half had suffered moderate erosion before building of the jetty. The ridge bears the tip of a small recessional parabola on its summit.

The spit is very similar to that at Netarts Bay. At the north end there are forested remnants almost to the tip. The principal dune masses are characterized by trough-blowout forms oriented northwest-southeast, in all stages from vigorous activity to complete stabilization (A, B, C). One of these (A) is massive enough to be considered a small parabola. Its tip has been sheared off by tidal currents; two triangular cut faces terminate the stabilized lateral ridges. Rejuvenation has produced a strip of bare sand along its axis with an active slipface at the tip which will probably cut through to the bay. The southern portion of the spit is even more attenuate than at Netarts Bay.

Tillamook Bay, in view of its considerable tributary drainage area, must, unlike Netarts Bay, always have had an outlet. The reconstructed dune system would seem to preclude the possibility of its always having been where it is now, and the only logical place is at the south end of the bay.

The sandy portions of the coast between Cape Falcon and Cape Lookout have in recent years suffered extreme damage from winter storms. Destruction was greatest on the spit outside Tillamook Bay, but it also occurred northward at Manhattan and Rockaway, and was severe southward on the spit at Netarts Bay. Mr. Robert L. Brown of the U. S. Soil Conservation Service has supplied information concerning the recent history of the Tillamook spit. The Bayocean area was homesteaded in 1867, and the resort was established in 1907. Serious destruction began in 1932,[34]

---

[34] At the time of my visit in 1928 the outer face of the dune ridge, though obviously formed by wave erosion, was fairly well covered with brush and grass, and there were a few young pines and spruces upon it.

when the hotel was undermined. Two storms in January and February, 1939, cut through the road at the base of the peninsula and undermined a long stretch of it on the bluff farther north. Aerophotos made by the Corps of Engineers, U. S. Army, on April 28 of the same year, show plainly the washed-out roads, wrecked houses overhanging the bluff, and the break-through across the road (D) with a small delta in the bay behind. A later communication from Mr. Brown states that destruction still goes on (1954); there is, however, no indication that a new outlet will develop.

The break-through that brought into being the present outlet, as at Netarts Bay, came late in the history—certainly subsequent to destruction of most of the parabola complex. The thin southern portion of the spit, again as at Netarts, may be the barrier ridge that closed the old outlet, subsequently shifting inland as the shore receded.

LOCALITY 14: SILETZ BAY

Siletz Bay (Pl. 2, Locality 14) concludes the series of eight localities in Region II where dune masses are associated with bay or river mouths. At one extreme is Sand Lake with its massive compound parabola and extensive areas of rejuvenation. At Siletz Bay, at the other extreme, there is no parabola complex at all. Recalling the very small surviving remnant at Tillamook Bay, it may not be concluded that there never was one. The spit is similar to the others. It is almost bare at the north, with a mass of mobile sand derived from former stable dunes. The narrow remnant strip of forested dune is being truncated by the sea and invaded by small trough blowouts which, unlike those previously described, show no consistent orientation with either summer or winter wind. Three dune ridges (A, B, C), projecting out upon the flat strip that borders the bay, have at some earlier time been sliced off by tidal currents.

LOCALITY 18: CHINA CREEK

Immediately north of Heceta Head is a small truncated parabola complex (Pl. 2, Locality 18) that deserves attention because the direction of the controlling wind is the reverse of that for all localities farther north: the north-northwesterly of summer instead of the southwesterly of winter. The substratum is a terrace. The southernmost tongue of sand ascends the mountain slope to a height of 120 m. The frontal terrace cliff and the dune-sand bluff perched upon it are well stabilized at the south, and support even a few groups of trees; farther north they are less well covered. There is evidence that considerable portions of the vegetation cover have been stripped in very recent time.

The parabola complex comprises two units. The area of the northern is mainly deflation surface apparently determined by the terrace top; there is an eastern marginal ridge, steep on both sides, 12–15 m high. The southern unit is more massive and complex; the cut-off tips of two recessional parabolas are superposed upon the older.

OTHER LOCALITIES IN REGION II

Rockaway (Pl. 2, Locality 6) is similar to Neskowin Creek (Locality 11). A barrier beach lies close to the mountain front and probably rests on; downwarped terrace close to sea level. Upon it there is a low, narrow dune ridge, fairly continuous, clothed with pine forest, eroding on its outer face. Behind this are several small lakes and ponds in dammed depressions of the terrace surface. Unlike Neskowin, the mountain front is nowhere cliffed. The sea at its maximum stand, just before progradation began, must therefore have barely touched it. The storms of 1939 did some damage here, but strikingly less than at Bayocean immediately to the south, possibly because of recent widening of the beach due to building of the jetty at the entrance to Tillamook Bay. This and Localities 5 and 7, north and south of it, make a continuous strip of sandy shore filling the re-entrant between Cape Falcon and Cape Meares.

Locality 12 is a small dune complex on a flat of limited extent at the mouth of the Salmon River. It agrees with the general rule: completely stabilized dunes inland and active ones advancing upon them from the beach.

Between Salmon River and the outlet of Devil's Lake are three narrow segments of dune perched at the top of the frontal terrace cliff (Locality 13). For the most part they are stabilized, but in a few places erosion is working in from the cliff edge. They are completely cut off from source of supply.

Locality 17 (Tenmile Creek) is another small perched dune mass. Several soil horizons in its eroding face indicate a complex history.

DISCUSSION: REGION II

Maintenance of dune activity requires access to a favorable shore frontage: a beach for reception of sand from the sea, with low-lying or gently sloping country behind it over which the wind-propelled sand can move easily. Such a situation may be conveniently termed a "receptive shore." The major dune masses of Region II have for a long time been based on rather narrow receptive sectors, and these are shown by projection of the parabola axes to have been some distance south-southwest of the existing remnants, beyond the present shore line. In half the cases (Localities 5, 7, 10, 15, 16), the receptive sector and the dune system tributary to it originally lay outside the lower course of a river or a bay, which emptied into the ocean at the south end of the sector. In two of these (7, 15) a new outlet at the north end replaced the original one rather late in the history. In Locality 10 a similar shift seems imminent today. The present mouths in Localities 8 and 9, where there is no relation to river valleys, are due to break-throughs at a comparatively recent time.

The fundamental features of the dunes in Region II were established during the period of the latest major submergence[35] and the differential recession of the coast line associated with it. During this period the dunes advanced inland from the sectors where effective contact with the beaches was maintained. With the single exception of Locality 18, the southwest winds of winter have been the controlling force, and the direction of invasion has been consistently within the octant north-northeast. The sand moved first over a substratum close to sea level, then onto a terrace or in some cases a short distance up a mountain slope. Activity gradually slackened and finally ceased at the line where the innermost stabilized ridges stand today.

The sea continued to advance, and the stabilized dune masses were truncated by it; the amount of truncation ranges from that in Locality 9, where most of the structure is still intact, to that in Locality 7, in which only a small fragment of the parabola

---

[35] Here and elsewhere the terms "submergence" and "emergence" connote process rather than state.

complex survives. Masses that had reached elevated situations were immune to direct attack by waves and resistant to wind. The bars and spits, easily erodible, were gradually narrowed by the waves. Dune masses upon them were penetrated by trough blowouts and reduced to a narrow strip, only fragments of which have survived. In this process the effective agent was not the southwesterly winter wind but the northerly wind of summer.

The period of submergence has been followed by a time characterized by comparatively stable sea level, with minor fluctuations such as those described for Locality 11. There are indications that the most recent change in sea level has been lowering, very small in comparison with the earlier rise, but significant in that the evidence for it is widely distributed, occurring both on the open coast and on the inner shores of spits and bars.

On open coast, sea cliffs formed at the maximum of advance are in places separated from the shore by barrier beaches carrying dunes and having bog areas and lakes behind them (Locality 11; Sears Lake in Locality 9; Locality 6); stabilized, often forested bluffs cut in both terrace and dune materials, with wide beaches in front, have for a considerable time been free from serious wave attack (Localities 5, 7, 8, 9, 18).

On the inner shores of spits and bars the water in the bays at maximum sea level washed against the inner slopes of already stabilized dunes and invaded the reentrants in them (Localities 7, 8, 9, 14); the ends of certain projecting structures were cut off by tidal currents (notably in Locality 14; also quite certainly in Locality 7, although here very recent cutting makes earlier events not quite so sure). Material deposited through gentle tidal circulation buried the bases of the dunes, some of which had been truncated. The apronlike strip that commonly borders the dunes on the inner side of spits and bars is assumed to be evidence of slight lowering since the maximum of advance of the sea.

The forward surge of the sand masses that ended with stabilization at their present inner margins, designated as Episode I, has been followed by others of lesser intensity. In two localities (5, 9) a second advance, designated Episode II, is conspicuous; there are possible but inconclusive traces of it in other localities. In the recent past the forces of destruction have been in the ascendance over those promoting stabilization, and this phase may be regarded as Episode III. Current activity in the parabola complexes is limited to those localities where there is still open communication with receptive shore (5, 9, 10, 16). The active areas for the most part take the form of a narrow strip lying along the axis of the parabola. Episode III may, nevertheless, develop into the most important readvance since stabilization of the outermost, oldest parabolas. In Locality 9 the mobile sand has not only broken through the tip of the parabola of Episode II but has overpassed on a wide front the stabilized lee slope of the oldest one. In Localities 10 and 16 the final ridge has been reached; only in Locality 5 has the current advance fallen short.

REGION III: COOS BAY DUNE SHEET
GENERAL FEATURES

The portion of the coast included in Region III is essentially a single unit; the dunes associated with it are so extensive and continuous that the designation "Coos

Bay dune sheet" is appropriate. So large and varied a unit cannot be adequately treated as a whole, and subdivision has therefore been made into five localities, nos. 19–23 (Pl. 3).

The Coos Bay dune sheet rests upon a lengthy strip of terrace that occupies a re-entrant in the mountain front bounded by two headlands about 96 km apart: Heceta Head-Sea Lion Point on the north and Cape Arago on the south. The terrace substratum is everywhere below sea level at the shore, because of normal seaward slope or local downwarp. The dune sheet itself has a frontage of 86 km, and its shore is a beach describing a smooth, gentle curve concave seaward, unbroken by a single rock exposure. Two major rivers cross it: the Siuslaw, with a drainage area extensive for a Coast Range stream, and the Umpqua, whose watershed extends to the divide of the Cascade Mountains. Coos Bay, an estuary receiving the waters of Coos River and several small streams, bounds the dune sheet on the south.

The great extent and continuity of receptive shore backed by terrain favorable to dune migration give ample opportunity for development of materials and forces. Because of the profusion of significant features it possesses, the field work concerned with forms and processes was concentrated here, and much material based upon it has already been presented.

LOCALITY 19: SIUSLAW RIVER NORTH

Extent and character.—Locality 19 (Pl. 3; Pl. 17, fig. 2) between Sea Lion Point and the Siuslaw River, has a total length of 16 km but ocean frontage of only 10 km; the southern 6 km is overlapped by the northward-projecting peninsula outside the Siuslaw River which belongs with Locality 20. The dune sheet for two-thirds of its length is more than 3 km wide, and the maximum is 4.5 km; this is the farthest inland invasion by dune masses anywhere in the field of study. Perhaps in part because they are spread over so great a breadth, the individual masses do not in general have the height or bulk attained in certain other parts. The same is true of Locality 23 at the other end of the dune sheet. Localities 19 and 23, because of great breadth of the dune belt, provide a fuller history than do the others, and they are therefore considered first.

Substratum.—The terrace substratum is accessible within the limits of the dune sheet at only one point, near the center (altitude 35 m), where gravel is exposed. Along the east bank of the Siuslaw below Florence the dunes rest upon beds of alluvial sand essentially at sea level that contain abundant remains of an ancient floodplain forest. Along the ocean shore the waves cut into the sand mantle itself; dune structure is visible on deflation surfaces down to within 1 m of high-tide level. A fair-sized stream fed by several tributaries rising in the mountains flowed across the northern end of the area previous to its burial by dune sand. The bottoms of Sutton and Mercer Lakes, ponded portions of its headwaters, are, respectively, 1 and 2 m below sea level. Otherwise the terrace was almost undissected. Collard, Clear, and Munsel Lakes are due to marginal ponding by dune masses.

Dune-sand mantle.—The most immediately obvious features are the areas of bare, mobile sand which contrast so strikingly with the general cover of forest. More important, however, in analysis of the general history are the stabilized features, comprising systems of ridges and intervening areas of low relief. The ridges are mainly of the type designated "precipitation ridges." Their continuity is frequently interrupted or obscured by moving sand, but general reconstruction of the pattern is possible in most places.

Beginning at the northern end is a single complex, 5 km long, which includes several ridges parallel to the mountain front. South of Sutton Lake the complex splits into two systems with generally north-south orientation. Between them there is a plain of low relief and a similar one between the western system and the ocean and river.

NORTHERN RIDGE COMPLEX: The innermost ridge of the complex is continuous for a long distance and is responsible for ponding of several small valleys. It has recently been overpassed locally by active sand. Much of the northern part of the complex has been destroyed, but small remnants in straight lines mark the positions of former intertrough ridges. A broad projecting tongue of forested dune is obviously a part of the complex. Its preservation is due to Sutton Creek, which, issuing from the stabilized area, passes across its front and carries away the sand that would otherwise pile up in the forest.

EASTERN RIDGE SYSTEM: From the area south of Sutton Lake where the ridge complex splits, the eastern system trends east-southeastward for 2 km; its inner limit is set by Mercer and Sutton Lakes and the stream connecting them. The trend is then southward parallel to the mountain front for 8 km to the Siuslaw River, thence along the river bank to the town of Florence. This portion of the system divides naturally into two units with similar histories; the point of division is marked by a gap in the ridgy topography opposite Munsel Lake. In the northern unit the old stabilized ridges have been almost completely buried or destroyed in the course of comparatively recent rejuvenation. The southern unit differs in that recent sand invasion has not gone so far, so that the two innermost ridges are still intact.

It is clear that antedating the period of recent rejuvenation there existed along the inner edge of the sand sheet a system made up of several roughly parallel precipitation ridges. The easternmost members, the oldest, were completely stabilized; the western, somewhat younger, retained areas of incomplete stabilization and were thus vulnerable to the factors inducing rejuvenation.

CENTRAL PLAIN: The central plain extends from the point where the eastern and western ridge systems split, southward 9 km to the Siuslaw River at Florence. Its width varies from .8 to 1.6 km. Most of the surface is flat, but there are a few isolated hills and ridges showing no systematic arrangement. The plain is completely stabilized and densely forested. It is essentially a deflation surface that has developed behind the advancing ridges of the eastern system.

WESTERN RIDGE SYSTEM: This consists of a principal ridge with shorter ones associated at certain points. The windward flanks of the northern half are marked by areas of active sand, which spills over the stabilized crest in a number of places. The conspicuous bare area southward marks an eastward shift of the principal ridge through rejuvenation currently in progress. The extreme southern portion of the principal ridge is intact except that it has been truncated by a northward swing of the river. An older ridge, very lobate, stands east of the main one, and a younger ridge west of it has also been truncated by the river.

OUTER PLAIN: This is essentially a deflation surface related to the western ridge system. In the northern part, bordering directly on the ocean, there has been much destruction of the earlier stabilized surface; a considerable portion is today a sea of transverse ridges. The southern part is very flat, with few prominent features, and it has been shaved away by the river on its western margin.

History of the dune sheet in Locality 19.—The history in Locality 19, so far as it is accessible, comprises three episodes of dune advance, the first two followed by periods of quiescence, the third now in active progress. Each advance had its origin from causes operating at the shore, which in each case gave rise to a train of events that, with locus constantly shifting inland, has continued to the present day.

EPISODE I: The earliest advance for which there is evidence was initiated at the shore, presumably with erosion of earlier stabilized masses and accession of new material from the beach. It was continued in the building of precipitation ridges and advance of these inland. In the course of the advance vegetation closed in behind and cut off the supply of sand, after which further progress was the result of repeated turnover with incorporation of materials from older dune masses if such existed in the path of invasion. The advance, its direction determined by the two seasonal winds in combination, was on a wide front. It covered the level terrace almost completely and ceased where formidable obstacles were encountered: forested mountain slopes on the northeast and east, the river on the southeast. Stabilization along this line brought establishment of the inner, older part of the northern complex and the eastern system with its final, oldest ridge and its several recessional ridges. Marginal lakes, several of considerable size, came into being through damming of valleys.

It is unlikely that a primary precipitation ridge, cut off from the source of supply at the shore, should advance so great a distance from beach to mountain front in a single uninterrupted march. In view of the powerful pressure toward stabilization constantly exerted by vegetation, these ridges in order to maintain their advance have probably undergone repeated rejuvenation. The extensive areas of mobile sand existing today at the inner margin of the dune sheet, the product of the latest rejuvenation, demonstrate that the train of events initiated long ago at the shore has not yet reached its conclusion.

Parabola dunes occur in Region III at the four points where the essential condition exists—obstruction of one of the seasonal winds, allowing the other to dominate. An imposing single parabola is found in Locality 19 at the farthest northeast extension of the dune sheet (Pl. 3, Locality 19, *A*). It is well protected from the summer wind but fully open to the southwest gales of winter. It attained its present state through repeated cycles of rejuvenation and stabilization. Flanking ridges and a rounded bulge projecting into Mercer Lake represent the first recognizable stage in its building. The apex of the main mass attains an altitude of 110 m, and its convex terminal face descends in a smooth slope more than 85 m, almost to the shore of the lake. Nested within the windward hollow is a small recessional parabola with a narrow tongue of mobile sand at its tip having a terminal slipface 20 m high—the last vestige of former intense activity. At the windward base of the parabola is an active slipface belonging to the extensive area of rejuvenation existing there; a moderate advance of this might initiate rejuvenation of the whole parabola.

The great age of the main structure is suggested by its forest cover. On the outer slope is a fire-killed stand of Douglas fir with trunks up to 2.2 m in diameter. Trees of this size, judging from ring counts elsewhere, could have been no less than 500 years old. An equivalent stand still lives in the windward hollow. The postfire forest, for the most part Douglas fir 30 m tall, is probably about 100 years old. A minimum of 600 years of forest history, which was preceded by a period of gradual stabilization of the steep slope, and this in turn by a time of intense activity, is thus indicated. This sequence is only the latest in a series.

After departure from the shore of the youngest recessional ridges of the eastern system came a lengthy period of meager sand supply. The area behind the recessional ridges was swept almost bare and acquired a forest cover. The deflated forested area gradually extended itself eastward and increased in breadth, since for the time being there was no further sand invasion.

EPISODE II: After the period of quiescence came renewed activity at the shore, with increased sand supply and erosion of such dunes as existed there. New precipitation ridges advanced inland and encroached on the forested deflation area of Episode I, which shifted bodily eastward, becoming the central plain of today. Episode II has been less complex than its earlier counterpart; only one or two ridges were formed instead of several. Movement ceased before the ridges had progressed half way across the terrace; recent rejuvenation has brought some further advance on certain sectors.

A second period of quiescence followed during which a deflation surface, the outer plain, came into being between the ridges and the shore. Deflation here was not as complete as on the older central plain; stabilization was accomplished while straight intertrough ridges were still in existence, some of which are visible today.

EPISODE III: In the comparatively recent past there has been a new burst of activity at the shore. In the vicinity of Heceta Beach (Pl. 14, fig. 2, right foreground) destruction has barely begun. Stabilized surfaces that have been only slightly invaded by trough blowouts here border the shore, and these bear several old intertrough ridges that are cut off obliquely at the top of the beach. Immediately to the north (center foreground) destruction has been greater, and the relief, including features related to both stabilization and destruction, is exceedingly complex. There are pieces of the outer plain bearing old intertrough ridges, and remnants of the latter surrounded by moving sand. There are also elongated trough blowouts, wide corridors due to enlargement and coalescence of these, and extensive areas reduced to deflation base showing all stages of invasion by vegetation from pioneers to pine forest. In left foreground, and at the north end of the dune sheet (Pl. 7, fig. 2), there is active sand bearing the transverse-ridge pattern.

Two salients of deep invasion with axes aligned with the summer wind lie on either side of the northwestward-pointing peninsula already described (Pl. 3, Locality 19; Pl. 17, fig. 2). In both, successive waves of sand have advanced inland, each wave marked by a precipitation ridge which presumably has moved to its present position in a single continuous march. Behind the oldest of these, in each case, is an area reduced to deflation base, essentially bare next to the ridge where it has been most recently exposed, and forested further to windward. There has not been sufficient time for forest development in the areas vacated by ridges nearer the shore.

In the southern salient the innermost and oldest ridge (Pl. 3, Locality 19, *B*; Pl. 14, fig. 2; Pl. 15, fig. 1) is a bow-shaped structure 2 km long. Its northern extremity has reached a state of senescence with complete stabilization fast approaching. The active portion of the ridge is all but cut off from the shore by establishment of forest on the deflation area behind it. The only connection is a long corridor through which passes a meager amount of new sand (Pl. 3, Locality 19, *C*). This was formerly much wider and has been narrowed by the growth of forest, strip by strip, on the northeast side. Eventually it will be eliminated, after which advance of the ridge will be entirely by turnover of materials already present. A second wave of advance is represented by two short ridges, approximately in line, which may in time unite. The third wave is as yet of minor importance.

In the northern salient, also, three waves of advance are evident. The innermost ridge (Pl. 3, Locality 19, *D*) is very massive, has almost completely overwhelmed an older stabilized ridge, and at one point is encroaching upon Sutton Lake. For part of its length it forms the inner margin of the sand sheet. Sand supply has been completely cut off by forest that has grown up in its wake, which in turn is being invaded by the second wave. The third is merely a concentration and intensification of the transverse-ridge pattern that characterizes the sea of sand behind it; no precipitation ridge has developed because there is as yet no forest in its path. The three waves of advance indicate rhythmic variation in activity. Episode III, still in its early stages, is compounded of several minor events, distinct in space and time, which may later merge through overtake of the older ridges by the younger. If this is true of the latest episode it was doubtless equally so of the earlier ones.

REJUVENATION IN LOCALITY 19: The general process of rejuvenation has been described; it has been pointed out, too, that the event has probably happened repeatedly during the inland march of the ridges. At the present time in Locality 19 features associated with rejuvenation are very prominent—possibly more so than average for the entire history—and discussion of the process as it is occurring today will therefore aid in understanding events of the past.

The southern unit of the eastern system furnishes the most adequate data. Sand shifting eastward has almost overwhelmed ridge 3 (Pl. 3, Locality 19) of the stabilized system. It moved up the gentle windward slope and partially buried the trees growing on it. The bare sand surface acquired the transverse-ridge pattern. Passing over the crest of the old ridge, the new sand settled upon the old lee slope, producing a new slipface. Additional sand coming over the top caused thickening of the mass, and invasion of the forest beyond ridge 3 began. In the meantime, locally on the western slope and summit, the old forest floor was exposed and the podzol cut through. In places the ridge was thereby decapitated.

It is necessary to account for the sand that has buried the major portion of ridge 3, and the source must obviously be a mass standing well above deflation base west of the buried ridge. A precipitation ridge, even one approaching stabilization if it still retains vulnerable spots, fits the requirements. There are apparent remnants of such a ridge, logically situated, which may be numbered 4. Ridge 4 is definitely present behind ridge 3 at its south end where it parallels the river bank. Westward from the north end of ridge 3 is a group of remnant hills crowned by a few living trees (4?). The strip connecting these with the southern remnant has been reduced to deflation base, quite recently in comparison with the central plain immediately to the west. It thus appears that rejuvenated ridge 4, leaving behind only fragments at its extremities, advanced up and over ridge 3. The deflation area in its wake now bears forest in the older parts and pioneer vegetation in the younger.

Two other extensive areas of rejuvenation have had similar histories. The one in the northern unit of the eastern system differs in that the moving sand has over-passed all earlier ridges that stood in its way and now lies at the inner edge of the dune sheet, invading the marginal lakes. Soil layers with dead trees rooted in them, overwhelmed by sand, are evidence of a buried ridge or ridges. The area of rejuvena-tion in the western system is invading the flat central plain rather than overwhelming older ridges.

Because of the importance of fire to the process of rejuvenation, an attempt was made to work out the recent fire history in Locality 19. At least 90 per cent of the whole is covered by even-aged stands of lodgepole pine, which, in addition to its role as pioneer, is the characteristic fire tree of the region. Its relation to fire over most of this area is confirmed by abundance of burned wood beneath the forest litter and on podzol surfaces buried and later exposed. A large number of ring counts widely distributed gives evidence of two fires. On the outer plain average age of the pines (using the oldest of several counts in a given locality, the date of reference being 1941), was 79.9 years, the oldest of all being 99 years. On the central plain and eastern system the average was 69.5 years and the oldest 71 years. The last fire on the outer plain thus occurred shortly before 1840 and on the central plain and eastern system shortly before 1870. Between them they swept the area almost completely bare. Resident Indians told of two fires about 80 and 100 years before 1933. Destruction is said to have been so complete that the ocean was visible from the interior dune ridges.

Patches of older forest are found around the fringes of the plain along the moun-tain front and river and bordering the ocean. The species are Douglas fir, spruce, and hemlock, rather than pine, and average age of the oldest trees in 11 localities was 167.7 years; the oldest accurate count was 210 years (year of reference 1941). These patches of forest made up of climax and near-climax species necessitate the assumption of a preceding generation of pine. The total length of time required for development from pioneers to present youthful climax has therefore been ±300 years. A fire at some time during the 17th century is indicated. If the rate of sand advance presented elsewhere is of the right order of magnitude, the three great areas of rejuvenation could not possibly have come into being in the time that has elapsed since the latest fires of record. These could only have stimulated into greater activity processes already under way. The earlier fire preceding the older forest may possibly have been the initiating cause of present activity or, far more likely, it may, like the later ones, have acted merely as a stimulus to a process tracing back still farther into the past.

LOCALITY 23: COOS BAY

Extent.—Locality 23 (Pl. 3; Pl. 17, fig. 3), at the southern end of the Coos Bay dune sheet, is considered next because in its main features it is most closely related to Locality 19. It extends from Tenmile Creek southward about 25 km to the outlet to Coos Bay. Approximately the southern third is occupied by a long sand spit exterior to the outlet. Maximum breath is 3.5 km.

Substratum.—At the northern end, from Tenmile Creek to Hauser, the inner edge of the sand plainly rests on a terrace surface, which at Saunders Lake is about 20 m above sea level; at the shore it is below sea level. South of Hauser the dune sheet is separated from the mountain front by a narrow depression comprising North Slough and a strip of salt marsh. The very lowest deflation surfaces show dune structure, and the assumption is justified that the mass outside North Slough is a body of dune sand partly submerged.

Dune-sand mantle.—Locality 23 is like Locality 19 in possessing ridge systems and deflation plains that point to a series of episodes in development of the dune sheet.

MARGINAL STABILIZED RIDGE SYSTEM: A narrow strip representing a system of forested precipitation ridges extends from Tenmile Creek to the inner edge of the dune sheet where it touches the Coos Bay outlet. It is everywhere undergoing active invasion from the west. North of Hauser it is almost continuous; southward, invasion has gone so far that only isolated fragments survive. In the northern portion there is proof of far greater westward extension of the stabilized masses in former times. Many remnant hills and some fairly extensive ridgy masses standing to seaward indicate that the system was once in places more than 1 km wide. At the southern end of the dune sheet where it borders the Coos Bay outlet are a number of ridges of considerable size aligned with the summer wind that antedate the eastern active system. They include half-canoe-shaped structures, some with smaller ones nested within them, and regular straight ridges, possibly parabola arms truncated by the currents of the outlet. Their relations are obscure, but they are most reasonably placed with the marginal stabilized system. On the spit that lies outside the outlet are several remnant stabilized masses that probably belong with the marginal system.

EASTERN ACTIVE RIDGE SYSTEM AND ITS ASSOCIATED DEFLATION PLAIN: Closely bound to the marginal stabilized ridge system is the massive active system that is invading it. Except for a single break in the middle it is continuous from Tenmile Creek to Coos Bay outlet. In its northern portion the active system falls short of the inner edge of the dune sheet, but in the southern part it is marginal to it except where a few isolated remnants of stabilized dunes have resisted its advance. The system may fairly be considered as an extended precipitation ridge with a series of oblique ridges attached to it. The latter conform to the type as already described. Their length is variable; the average of 24 is 600 m. Maximum altitude ranges up to 43 m and height above immediate base to 36 m. Between them are deep re-entrants lying at the same level as the deflation plain to the west; their surfaces are saturated in winter and some even acquire temporary ponds. Inward the level in the re-entrant gradually rises to the col between the bulging ridge ends, beyond which is the inland-facing slipface.

Between the eastern and western active ridge systems lies a plain of low relief continuous from Tenmile Creek almost to the Coos Bay outlet. Essentially it is a deflation plain related to the eastern active ridge system; reduction, however, is far from complete. Processes going on are constantly transforming details without altering its essential character. Along the outer edge of the plain the forest is being invaded and destroyed by advance of the outer active ridge system; along the inner edge it is advancing over the areas vacated by the inner active system. The plain is slowly shifting eastward.

In contrast to Locality 19, fire has played a very minor part in the history. There are no signs anywhere of burned forest on the present surfaces. At three points in the northern portion old charred wood has been uncovered, and in the eroding face of one remnant mass four superposed podzolic horizons all showed signs of fire. In the southern part of the plain not a single sign of fire has been discovered, ancient or modern. Certain areas have been subjected to grazing, but the effect has been merely a local intensification of sand movement.

Locality 23 possesses a feature unique for the Coos Bay dune sheet in the occurrence of lakes entirely within its limits as distinguished from marginal lakes, which

TABLE 7.—*Dune lakes in Locality 23: height above sea level of water surface and bottom*
August 23–24, 1948

Number of lake on Pl. 3, Loc. 23	Name		Water surfae above sea level (meters)	Depth (meters)	Bottom above sea level (meters)
	Topo. Map	Local			
1	Horsfall	....	6.17	1.55	4.62
2	....	Spirit	6.17	1.31	4.86
3	....	....	6.17	1.13	5.04
4	Sandpoint	Sandpoint	6.17	1.55	4.62
5	....	Shoestring	6.17	1.89	4.28

are common. All but one occur upon the deflation plain, most of them in a close group in the southern part where it is widest. Several are of considerable size; the dimensions of the largest (Horsfall Lake) at the end of the rainy season of 1940–1941 were 500 by 1500 m. Local residents stated that all but one went completely dry in 1924 and once or twice since. These lakes, though obviously shallow, lie so very low' that it seemed desirable to determine exactly the height of their bottoms above sea level.[36] The results of the survey are given in Table 7. A well boring near the shore of one of the lakes, where the ground surface was at 8.1 m, is reported to have struck a layer of plant remains at a depth of 4.3 m, or 3.8 m above sea level— lower than the bottom of any of the lakes.

Beale lake, north of the main group, is higher. Its water surface in 1928 was at

[36] The work was done by Mr. K. N. Phillips of Portland, Oregon, and Dr. and Mrs. D. B. Lawrence of the University of Minnesota on August 22–24, 1948. A line of transit levels was run from a bench mark on the railroad to the lakes. Many soundings were made from a boat, the deepest of which are given in the table. I wish to express my appreciation of the assistance given to Mr. Phillips and Dr. and Mrs. Lawrence by Dr. George E. Dix of Coos Bay, who provided the boat, Mr. Arch B. Sanders of Coos Bay, and Mr. Phillips, caretaker for Dr. Dix.

10.4 m and the bottom in the deepest part at 7.7 m (soundings by author). This lake too has been known to go dry in recent years.

All the lakes contain, except in the deepest parts, numerous dead pine trunks and stumps, which imply a period of low lake levels and therefore a generally low water table for 2–3 decades at least. No such period has occurred in the memory of local residents, but the fact that the stumps have not rotted away indicates comparative recency.

WESTERN ACTIVE RIDGE SYSTEM: This has already been described in connection with the oblique-ridge pattern (Fig. 9; Pl. 12, fig. 3). The system is everywhere invading the flat deflation area and burying the youthful forest that grows upon it. That this forest and therefore the deflation plain associated with the eastern active-ridge system recently extended beyond the western system almost to the shore is proved by a zone of dead pines and frequent living spruces projecting from the moving sand; a group of still-living spruces, partly buried and exhumed, the oldest 70 years of age, 500 m from the beach; and an exposure of podzol with small pine stumps only 400 m from the beach.

LITTORAL ZONE: Outside the western ridge system is a strip of sand lying barely above sea level, for the most part 300–500 m wide. Without doubt the whole strip would be covered with transverse ridges were it not for the recent appearance of marram grass, which has become well established throughout the length of Locality 23, producing a definite foredune zone 100 m wide.

History of the dune sheet in Locality 23.—There is evidence here, as in Locality 19, of three episodes of advance. The visible results of the first are the marginal stabilized ridge system and the isolated masses and remnant hills that stand to seaward of it. These denote a system of ridges at least 1 km wide which, in turn, implies the existence of a forested deflation strip to seaward, evidence of which has been destroyed.

The second episode, reasoning from the processes going on today in the third advance, began when increase in sand supply at the shore caused formation of precipitation ridges at the edge of the forest. Oblique ridges were added, and the system moved inland. Having passed over the assumed deflation plain, the advancing front invaded the stabilized ridge system, destroyed most of it, and appropriated its materials. A few remnant masses survived. Reduction behind the front was not complete, and activity has continued locally and intermittently ever since. This instability may perhaps be traced to greater than usual fluctuations in the water table, due in turn to the fact that much of the dune area is cut off from direct surficial contact with the mainland and thus presumably receives no steady stabilizing flow of ground water from it. Certainly, during lengthy periods of low precipitation, deflation has reduced extensive areas, at the time bare of vegetation, to a level lower than the general. In times of at least average precipitation these depressions contain lakes.[37]

The second major advance has overpassed the ultimate ridges in many places. Still retaining much of its original vigor, it may do so all along the line.

---

[37] The wide fluctuation in depth of water table in the southern part of Locality 23 and the voluminous flow of underground water currently being extracted by the Pacific Power and Electric Company from the same area cannot at present be reconciled.

There is a suggestion as to the age of Episode II in the estimated rate of shift of the eastern active-ridge system at a point in Locality 23. Distance from the windward edge of the system to the beach is 1050 m. With an average annual rate of 1.6 m, about 650 years would be required to cover this distance, plus an unknown length of time during which there was no movement.

The third episode of advance, represented by the western active ridge system, is still in its early stages. The forest that is being invaded by its slipfaces is young, and the dead pines and the few living spruces that stand in its wake are apparently of the same generation. The future of the western ridge system will be like that of the eastern but on a lesser scale—unless there is a pronounced increase in supply of new sand. The eastern system owes most of its great bulk to materials incorporated from older masses; the western has as yet far less to draw upon.

LOCALITY 22: UMPQUA RIVER SOUTH

Extent and character.—Locality 22 (Pl. 3; Pl. 18, figs. 1, 2), continuous with the last, extends from Tenmile Creek north to the Umpqua River, approximately 10 km. Width of the dunes mostly exceeds 2 km; the maximum is 3.5 km. In magnitude of dune features and therefore scenically it is the most impressive part of the dune sheet; the expanse of active sand is here widest and the oblique ridges reach their greatest size. The dunes, viewed from the shore, have an apparent height of more than 160 m, though actual thickness of sand is considerably less.

Substratum.—Locality 22 differs profoundly from Locality 23 in that the substratum, below tide for a short distance only, rises rapidly inland. The most prominent feature of subdune relief is a north-south ridge which constitutes the divide between the ocean and a valley now for the most part buried by sand but in its upper northern portion containing Clear Lake. Height of the ridge near its north end, where it emerges from beneath the sand, is 111 m. Southward its crest descends and broadens; the seaward slope is gentler than the inner. Tertiary sedimentary rocks constitute the core, but the material upon which the dune sand actually rests, wherever visible on the seaward slope, is consolidated terrace sand.

Dune-sand mantle.—The structure of the dune sheet in Locality 22 is simpler than in Localities 19 and 23. It consists of an inner stabilized strip with a few related remnant masses standing far out and an outer zone of deep, extremely active sand comprising 80 per cent of the total area.

STABILIZED DUNES: The stabilized, forested strip is almost unbroken. At various points 1–3 precipitation ridges are evident. West and southwest of Clear Lake a giant parabola complex is superposed upon one or two older ridges (Pl. 18, fig. 2). The forest on the stabilized dunes is mature or submature; well-developed climax occurs on lee slopes, especially in sheltered re-entrants. Four Douglas firs evenly spaced along the forested strip, all near the edge of the active sand, gave age counts of 226, 223, 250, 230 years. Signs of fire are few and local, and plainly related to recent lumbering activities.

The above-mentioned parabola complex is the most massive of all in the field of study. It is like those of Region II in orientation of the units, in that it was built by stages, and in the slicing off of its western flank by the sea. It differs in having no prominent recessional structures. The cut face is a very straight, steep bluff 2 km long and 90–110 m high (Pl. 18, fig. 3). There are five closely placed parabola units. The longest is directly behind the bluff, and part of its western arm has been cut away. It points almost exactly north. Passing southeastward, the second unit at its apex attains an altitude of 168 m and a height of 57 m above the terrace substratum on which it rests. The third unit descends to the shore of Clear Lake, and the fourth and fifth approach it closely. Each parabola contains a long narrow strip of mobile sand opening out to the bare expanse beyond.

OPEN SAND: This comprises three divisions: the zone of oblique ridges, the area of transverse ridges, and the littoral zone. The oblique ridges have already been fully treated with respect to their character and the factors that control their development. It remains to consider them as an integral part of this particular dune complex.

The zone of oblique ridges in Locality 22 is a direct continuation of the eastern active ridge system of Locality 23. It is, however, much broader, and occupies most of the area of open sand. The ridges are longer and more massive. At its north end the zone is in contact with the littoral strip; southward it recedes and a wedge-shaped area dominated by the transverse-ridge pattern occupies the space between it and the littoral strip. There is no western active ridge system. The littoral zone comprises a marram-grass foredune and a deflated strip behind it.

History of the dune sheet in Locality 22.—This locality possesses by far the greatest amount of dune sand per unit of shore frontage, the obvious reason being that the Umpqua River, which has a much larger drainage area than any other between the Columbia and the Rogue, with no significant settling basin at its mouth, empties into the ocean immediately to the north. The appearance is of two major dune advances.

FIRST MAJOR DUNE ADVANCE: As the whole shore is receptive, inland advance was on a wide front. It is probable that then, as now, the oblique ridge was the characteristic form, though in the early stages on a smaller scale. Advance was most rapid and inland penetration greatest at the southern end where elevation of the substratum is low; distance covered was least at the north end, where the sand had to ascend the steep slope of a ridge more than 100 m high. The resulting configuration of the advancing front thus brought increasing shelter from the northerly summer winds and left control to the southwesterly gales of winter. The natural result was the building here of a great parabola complex.

Inland invasion eventually ceased all along the line. Lesser advances produced recessional ridges and added to the mass of the parabola complex. Stabilization ultimately extended at least as far seaward as the remnant masses of today, and probably almost to the shore.

After stabilization of the oldest dune masses had been accomplished the sea continued its encroachment upon the land (*cf.* similar cases in Region II). The extreme limit of its advance is set at the base of the high wave-cut bluff bounding the outermost parabola unit. The dense forest that clothes it and the wide sandy strip bearing small oblique ridges that lies in front prove that it has been immune from wave attack for a long time and suggest the probability of slight recession of the sea. A line continuing the base of the bluff, projected southward in a gentle arc concave seaward, sets the limit for transgression by the sea all the way to the Coos Bay outlet.

SECOND MAJOR ADVANCE: Events associated with renewal of activity presumably followed in general the course outlined for the eastern active ridge system of Locality 23: precipitation ridges at the seaward edge of the forest followed by development of oblique ridges which extended themselves inland and constantly gained in mass by incorporation of older materials. As they ascended the seaward slope of the north-south ridge an important difference from Locality 23 appeared: as deflation base is the surface of the substratum, the corridors between the ridges were in many places swept bare of sand. Frequently these areas have remained bare long enough to permit development of vegetation, even to the extent of patches of small pine and spruce; certain ponds have acquired considerable amounts of aquatic vegetation. The hold that plants maintain is, however, precarious; isolated spruces with living tops show where an area of exposure has been buried by a shift of neighboring sand masses.

The greatest thickness of sand occurs where the inner ends of the ridges stand over the filled-in valley of ancestral Clear Creek (Fig. 10). On ridge *A-A* of Figure 10 maximum thickness is about 90 m. Even in the corridor *B-B*, just south, depth to the bottom of the valley is about 60 m.

The conspicuous forest-crowned remnant masses, facing constant attack by wind, are steadily diminishing in volume. On the seaward side there is frequently a deep curving trough excavated by a concentrated current, which in a series of dry seasons is deepened beyond the average plane of the water table and later acquires a pond that may last for many years. While a remnant is eroding on one side it may be building on another. Waves of sand move up its flank, usually from the north or northwest and form a small precipitation ridge just within the forest edge. In this way height of the remnant may actually increase while area decreases. The process of attrition is extremely slow because of the rapidity with which vegetation colonizes fresh surfaces. A particular face exposed to the erosive effect of the winds for a time may become sheltered because of changes in distribution of neighboring mobile masses. Pines, even Douglas firs, quickly establish themselves in such places, which thereafter may remain stable for a long period. Activity of a precipitation ridge may diminish or cease and permit its surface to acquire a forest cover. Ages of a number of pines growing on erosion and deposition surfaces ranged from 77–105 years. Such an episode may be repeated many times. Every remnant, however, assuming continuance of the present general trend, must ultimately disappear; the smallest (3, Pl. 3, Locality 22) is already close to extinction.

The forest on all but the smallest of the remnants is essentially climax. Douglas fir and spruce are the largest; hemlock and arbor vitae occur on some. On remnant 4 grows a Douglas fir which with other evidence indicates the length of time that has elapsed since the surface at this point became stabilized. The growth history of this tree, which was 130 cm in outside diameter, was compared with that of one of similar size in an area of mature climax forest outside but near the dune margin (Locality 20, near Glenada). A core 27 cm long taken from the former covered approximately half the radius. A complete ring count of the latter was obtained from a cut stump 2 m above the ground; its total number of rings was 493. The data for the outer 27 cm of each are as follows:

	Number of rings	Average width of rings, mm
Tree on dune	376	0.72
Tree outside dunes	335	0.81

It may be assumed that the dune tree of slightly lesser diameter but with narrower rings is approximately the same age as the other—about 500 years. This gives the absolute minimum for the period since the dune surface was stabilized. There are indications of a considerably greater length of time: a dead stub of spruce nearly 2 m thick, very rotten; fallen trunks buried in thick moss; presence of plant species that do not become established until full climax status has been attained (notably Pacific yew, *Taxus brevifolia* Nutt.); and necessity of preparation for the climax by a pioneer stand of pine which commonly maintains itself for at least a century.

The parabola units have shared in the general renewal of activity. Since in a declining phase the last portion of the trough to retain activity is the bottom, where the converging wind currents are concentrated, rejuvenation begins here likewise. At the windward ends the sides of the troughs are being scoured and the peninsulas between them are receding; at the upper, leeward ends deposition is in progress. The southern two units are moderately active. The middle one has recently spilled over; masses of sliding sand reached the shore of the lake until artificial stabilization was instituted to protect the highway from burial. The next one north, though highest of all, shows definite signs of recent shrinkage of active sand. The lengthy active strip of the parabola next to the shore seems to be in a state of approximate equilibrium. At one place, however, sand has blown out of the trough over the ridge to the west and has descended the seaward slope nearly half way to the bottom (Pl. 18, fig. 3). If a complete break-through should occur here another forested remnant would come into being roughly in line with those southward.

Along its seaward border the oblique-ridge pattern is "in competition" with the transverse-ridge pattern. Other conditions being the same, abundant sand supply favors the former. Accordingly, at the northern end, nearest the mouth of the Umpqua, the oblique ridges extend almost to the shore—even beyond the line of the sea's farthest advance, as proved by the presence of several small ones at the base of the high wave-cut bluff. Transverse ridges here play a very minor role and are confined to the corridors between the major structures. Southward, with decreasing sand supply, the transverse ridges have increasingly asserted their dominance. They have overspread the seaward extremities of the oblique ridges, causing them to fan out southward. The zone of oblique ridges has thus receded increasingly southward leaving behind it a uniform expanse of transverse ridges. The supply of sand, however, has been sufficient, until introduction of marram grass, to prevent reduction to deflation base, and establishment of vegetation has therefore been impossible.

It is quite certain that before the advent of marram grass there was no foredune here. The grass has made rapid progress in recent years. In 1940 there was a zone of hillocks, rather well developed at Tenmile Creek, becoming narrower and sparser northward and ceasing at a point opposite remnant 2. A very narrow strip stabilized at deflation base was present behind the foredune zone. In 1953 there was a continu-

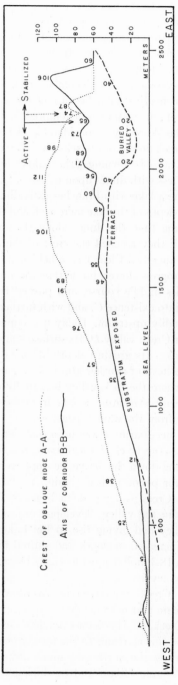

FIGURE 10.—*Longitudinal profiles along oblique ridge A-A and adjoining corridor B-B of Figure 7; approximate profile of substratum surface Distances measured along slightly curving crest of ridge and similar curve of corridor axis. Vertical scale 4 times horizontal.*

ous belt of densely placed hillocks all the way from Tenmile Creek to the mouth of the Umpqua. The deflation strip had lengthened and broadened and had acquired a dense vegetation cover, probably mostly salt rush. Establishment of forest is now possible here, and probably a few trees are already present.

DRAINAGE CHANGES ASSOCIATED WITH DUNE ADVANCE: During the grand period of submergence the drainage system of which Tenmile Creek is the main stem underwent an interesting process of readjustment because of the advance of the dunes in Locality 22. Reconstruction of the history is attempted in Figure 11 A, B, C, D. Early in the period, when the shore lay a considerable distance west of its present position, ancestral Tenmile Creek flowed out to sea in a valley cut across the terraced coastal slope, A. Submergence caused drowning of the main valley and the lower courses of its tributaries. A bar, doubtless with dunes upon it, formed across the river mouth, and the ponded valley became a lake with branches extending up the tributaries B. With continued submergence depth of the lake increased, and the arms were extended farther upstream. At the same time the dunes along the shore north of Tenmile Creek were advancing inland; they reached the crest of the north-south ridge and descended into the valley of ancestral Clear Creek behind it. The greatly increased extent of the slipface made progress slower, but in time the dunes, entering the valley broadside, advanced across its middle course, and pushed the stream up the east slope. Clear Lake now came into existence C, and with further advance and increase in depth of sand it shifted bodily upstream. Today it occupies the ramifying headwater extremities of the Clear Creek valley D. Its surface stands at 67 m, an unusual height for a dune-dammed lake. Its greatest depth, 32 m, is near the head of the longest arm; the depth at the head of another arm is only 2 m less.[38] The shallowest portion is at the lower end where the rock valley is actually deepest; this is due to the sand that has slid and been blown into the lake from the great blockading dune mass that rises 70 m directly from the water's edge.

The creek in its uphill shift necessarily flowed for a considerable distance along the advancing dune front, and as the level of Clear Lake rose its gradient increased. Large quantities of sand sliding down the active lee slope were carried downstream, in particular during the winter period of heavy rain. At the point where ancestral Clear Creek flowed into Eel Creek valley a delta began to form which, extending itself across the narrow lake in the valley, developed into a sand flat blocking off the upper portion of the valley and giving rise to Eel Lake C. As the barrier increased in height Eel Lake increased in depth and shifted upstream along its two branches. Its surface today is 18.3 m above sea level; its bottom at the deepest point measured lies 2.1 m below sea level.

The drainage from Clear Creek, reinforced by overflow from Eel Lake, now carried sand farther downstream and resumed delta formation in the lake occupying the main valley of Tenmile Creek, C. The delta extended itself across the lake to the south shore and upstream and downstream. In the former direction it made contact with the promontory separating the north and south arms, thus segregating the present North and South Tenmile Lakes, and producing the extensive sand flat upon which the village of Lakeside stands, D.

---

[38] Soundings by C. O. Morgan.

Dune activity now ceased along the middle course of Clear Creek, which was thus no longer provided with sand for delta building. Movement continued, however, farther south, and the dunes advanced over the surface of the stream-made flat. At one point the front reached the hilly mass between Eel and North Tenmile Lakes and cut the flat in two, *D*. Since complete cessation of movement and develop-

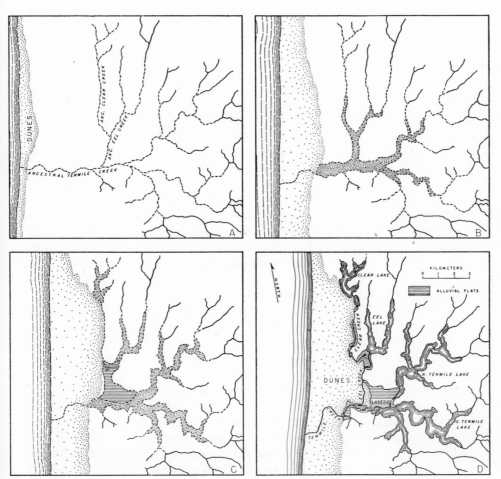

FIGURE 11.—*Modifications in Tenmile drainage system due to encroachment by dune belt during grand period of submergence*

A: shortly after beginning of submergence. *D:* present state. Broken lines: hypothetical stream courses and shores before the present.

ment of a forest cover all along the line, no further modifications of the drainage pattern have taken place. At unusually high flood levels, however, Clear Creek still carries sand from the base of an active ridge and deposits it on the Eel Creek flats. A few years ago half a meter of it was laid down on Highway 101 (C. O. Morgan, personal communication). As contact broadens between the active sand front and the creek, trouble for the highway will increase.

LOCALITY 21: UMPQUA RIVER NORTH

Extent and character.—Locality 21 (Pl. 3) extends from the Umpqua River north to Siltcoos River, 23 km. The southernmost 6 km is a peninsula outside the lower course of the Umpqua. The remainder is a narrow strip at the base of the mountain front except at Tahkenitch Creek, where there is a wider expanse of flat surface. The valley of Tahkenitch Creek has been dammed by dune advance to form Tahkenitch Lake, the several arms of which have been extended up the tributary valleys as submergence progressed. The level of the lake is now 1.5 m above tide, and its bottom at the deepest point lies 4.6 m below sea level.[39]

Substratum.—The dunes presumably rest upon a terrace surface. It is exposed only at the base of the Umpqua peninsula, where, on the river side, a fragment of sandy terrace material rests upon the rock platform which here stands at about 30 m. The peninsula itself probably has a rock core, though the attenuate tip is clearly of spit nature. At the shore the substratum is everywhere below sea level.

Stabilized dunes.—The inner strip of stabilized dunes is for the most part very narrow and in several places has been cut completely through. A few outlying remnants survive.

At the southern end of the dune belt a system has developed that is an almost exact counterpart of those characteristic of Region II. A massive parabola complex, considerably mutilated by recent erosion, lies in shelter from the summer winds. Its very high outer portion (64–75 m, almost all of which is dune sand) is close to the beach and is bounded by a wave-cut bluff, completely forested, that is in line with the one south of the Umpqua and almost as high. As in Region II, remnants of the system survive on the peninsula south of the complex.

At the mouth of Tahkenitch Creek is another parabola complex consisting of four very symmetrical and perfect units (Pl. 19, fig. 1). Three of them have outer slopes that attain a height of 60 m and support a well-developed climax forest except where sand from the active inner portion is spilling over. The units are so close together that the spaces between them are sharp ravines.

Open sand.—Infrequent short, poorly developed oblique ridges stand upon a narrow slope leading up to the bluffs bounding the stabilized masses. The wider expanse at Tahkenitch Creek bears several oblique ridges of fair size, and the open sand is continued in active tongues along the axes of the parabolas. North of Tahkenitch Creek is a narrow outer strip bearing the transverse-ridge pattern; south of it there is hardly room for such development. Here, as elsewhere, there has recently been enormous increase of marram grass resulting in building of a well-defined foredune.

History of the dune sheet in Locality 21.—During the grand period of submergence the gently concave shore line of the Coos Bay dune sheet, controlled in inland shift by the headlands at its northern and southern ends, here approached the mountain front most closely. Where the dunes of the first advance moved broadside against a regular stretch of mountain front, linear depressions were formed which now contain long narrow lakes parallel to the shore. The level of Carter Lake stands at

---

[39] Soundings by Oregon State Game Commission.

about 8 m, that of Threemile Lake, which is 2 km long and only 200 m wide, at 5 m. At a few other places ravines in the mountain front have been blocked by the advancing sand and small ponds have formed in them, some more than 50 m above sea level.

At the two points where invasion was not strictly limited the sand moved into shelter from one or the other of the seasonal winds, and the two parabola complexes developed as a result. The one at the base of the Umpqua peninsula followed the general rule in that its units, controlled by the winter winds, extended themselves in a northeasterly direction. The abundance of sand available for so massive a system may be attributed to proximity to the Umpqua River. Of the four units of the parabola complex at Tahkenitch Creek, three point southeastward. Explanation of this anomaly lies in movement of sand over a flat surface into an area sheltered from the southwest winter winds by an offset in the mountain front. It is evident that the summer winds, given freedom from interference, are just as effective as those of winter in building parabola structures.

During the ensuing period of quiescence, stabilization extended to the present line of the shore and probably beyond. The sea in its continued advance cut away a large portion of the southern parabola complex; the wide beach in front of the bluff suggests slight emergence in later time.

The second major advance has reduced the stabilized dune surface for the most part to a narrow strip. The manner of destruction is a variant of the general process, probably related to narrowness of the dune strip and abruptness of the mountain front behind it. Trough blowouts come into being at points of weakness, some controlled by the summer wind, others by the winter gale. Two near-by troughs, one advancing southeastward, the other northeastward, converge to a common point, and thus isolate a mass of stable dunes which itself decreases in area due to attrition and finally disappears. Where there are no significant points of weakness the dunes are worn back in fairly regular fashion, and a bluff results. Forest development may bring temporary stabilization, but converging troughs cut in from behind, and the mass is isolated and in time destroyed. New bluffs become stabilized, and new troughs develop through repetition of these processes.

At the points where the earlier advance was greatest, the present advance has also penetrated far beyond the average. At Tahkenitch Creek the area of mobile sand is wide, and the parabolas have undergone vigorous rejuvenation. The Umpqua peninsula has been swept almost clear, and the parabola complex at its base has been intricately dissected by trough blowouts, some of which have attained considerable size. Most of the blowouts here are due to the southwest gales of winter and therefore penetrate in a northeastward direction; some, however, are governed by the northerly winds of summer. Several masses have been isolated by intersecting troughs and others are approaching that state.

LOCALITY 20: SIUSLAW RIVER SOUTH

Extent.—Locality 20 (Pl. 3; Pl. 19, fig. 2) extends from Siltcoos River north to the Siuslaw River, a distance of 19 km. The northernmost part is a peninsula 6 km long outside the lower course of the Siuslaw. The main body ranges from 2.4 to 3.5 km in breadth.

Substratum.—The mountain front, near the shore in Locality 21, recedes abruptly north of Siltcoos River, and the terrace strip widens correspondingly; maximum distance from the shore to its inner edge is approximately 5.5 km. The dune sheet falls far short of covering its whole width; the uninvaded part is in places more than 2 km wide. More than one terrace level seems to be present here; much of the portion exposed behind the dunes is too high for the 30-m terrace and too maturely dissected, the original flat surface surviving only in limited areas on the interfluves.

Stabilized dunes.—For 4.5 km south of the Siuslaw River the older stabilized dunes have been very recently overwhelmed by the active sand of the second advance. From Cleawox Lake to Siltcoos River a narrow strip of stabilized dunes survives, broken through at only one point. Along its east margin is a precipitation ridge with areas of mildly active sand on its windward face, and west of this one or two discontinuous ridges of similar character. Most of the forest is of pine, indicating fire, but at least one area of mature Douglas fir exists, in which the highest ring count gave an age of a little more than 330 years.

As in Locality 22 a number of forested remnants stand well out in the open sand. The largest, at the mouth of Siltcoos River, matches a similar smaller one south of the river. Dead trunks 200 m farther out indicate recent destruction of the seaward portion. The other remnants are abrupt hills rising up to 45 m above their bases (Pl. 20, fig. 1). Their seaward slopes are for the most part moderate and even, and forested with Douglas fir 140–150 years old with streamlined crowns. The sides and backs are eroding and some have prominent wind troughs next to them.

Open sand.—About 90 per cent of the area is active sand, in which three zones may be distinguished. The innermost is characterized by a system of well-developed oblique ridges, the next by the transverse-ridge pattern; the third is the littoral strip.

The oblique ridges of this locality have been treated in the general discussion of the type (Pl. 13, figs. 1, 2). The precipitation ridge that binds together their landward extremities is conspicuous because distance between oblique ridges is considerable. In addition to the well-developed units are many subdued, ridgelike masses similar in length, spacing, and orientation to the others, and which have a superposed pattern of transverse ridges completely covering them.

The transverse-ridge zone is continuous through the whole length of the locality except where Cleawox Lake has intermittently discharged its waters to the sea. The pattern reaches its finest development here, and this locality has therefore been extensively utilized in the general discussion (Pl. 7, figs. 1, 3; Pl. 8, fig. 1). The zone is from 1 to 2.5 km wide. The littoral strip consists almost entirely of a marram-grass foredune composed of hillocks up to 8 m high. Inside it is a suggestion of a deflation strip, but for the most part the foredune is joined directly to the area of transverse ridges.

History of the dune sheet in Locality 20.—The Siuslaw River is second only to the Umpqua in extent of drainage area, and it has no settling basin. Accordingly, the dune masses immediately to the south are now and presumably have been throughout their history of more than average magnitude.

With dune advance during the period of submergence there came into being a group of sand-dammed marginal lakes. Siltcoos Lake, lying partly in the terrace strip and draining a small watershed in the mountains, is unique in that its main body is very broad—3 by 5 km—and also very shallow. Its surface is 1.5 m above tide, and its bottom at the deepest point lies 4.6 m below sea level.[40] Woahink Lake, just north of Siltcoos, lies entirely within the limits of the terrace strip. The stream that made its valley, before it was dammed, was probably a tributary of ancestral Siltcoos River. The lake surface is 11 m above tide; its bottom at the deepest point lies 12 m below sea level—the lowest of any of the sand-dammed lakes. Its watershed is extremely limited, and little sedimentation has taken place in it. Cleawox Lake was formed by ponding of the headwaters of a stream separate from the Siltcoos-Woahink system. Soundings show the tips of three small tributaries; the divides between them are submerged. Present surface is at 25 m; the bottom at the deepest point is 11.5 m above sea level. More than half its western shore is bordered by actively advancing dunes that have overpassed the earlier masses responsible for its formation.

As to the extreme limit of transgression by the sea there is no direct evidence for this locality. By reference to the shore-line curve indicated by the wave-cut bluffs of Localities 21 and 22 it may be set approximately at not more than 100 m behind the present shore.

The area of the masses stabilized during the period of quiescence that followed the first major advance can be approximated by adding to the evidence of the inner strip and the outlying remnants that supplied by numerous exposures of forest soil among the active dunes with dead trees rooted in them. It appears that a forested ridgy belt extended from the Siuslaw to Siltcoos River and seaward at least as far as the outermost remnant hills. Between this and the shore there must have been a deflation plain, also forested.

The second major advance doubtless involved the processes outlined for Localities 23 and 22—a precipitation ridge followed by a system of oblique ridges; irregular advance resulted in island remnants. With incorporation of older materials the oblique ridges became more pronounced, and some of them attained great size. Some have shifted their positions a little but not consistently in direction.

The manner of invasion where the second advance has overwhelmed the ridges of the first is well shown immediately south of the Siuslaw River. The new sand invades the windward slope of the older mass as a precipitation ridge, and a succession of waves follows it (Fig. 12; Pl. 20, fig. 2). The surface, now essentially free of obstacles, acquires the regular transverse-ridge pattern. Passing the crest of the old ridge, the sand falls on the stabilized lee slope which is here 25–40 m high. Whereas the sand on the windward slope, in constant motion, cannot accumulate to any considerable depth, that which goes over the top, after gravity has done its work, is completely at rest. The new sand covering the old lee slope is at first a mere veneer but it gradually increases in thickness and builds out to leeward. An active slipface has replaced the stabilized lee slope (Pl. 15, fig. 2). Advance is now very slow because the oncoming sand is distributed over a slipface of great breadth. Back on the windward slope local sand removal exposes areas of buried podzol which, once broken through, are subject to undermining and destruction.

---

[40] Soundings in Siltcoos, Woahink, and Cleawox Lakes by Oregon State Game Commission.

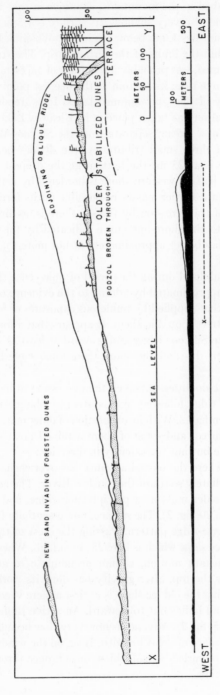

FIGURE 12.—*Profile across dune sheet, north end of Locality 20*

See Plate 19, Figure 2 and Plate 20, Figure 2. Below, whole width of dune sheet; horizontal and vertical scales the same. Above, the portion X-Y of lower profile; vertical scale twice the horizontal. Manner of invasion of stabilized dunes by a thin sheet of new sand.

As in Localities 21 and 22, there is no outer active ridge system of the type so well developed in Locality 23.

Advance of the active dunes shows no sign of slackening. For nearly half the distance the earlier limits have been overpassed. In the southern half invasion is steadily narrowing the still-surviving belt of stabilized dunes, which in 1940 ranged from less than 100 to 700 m in width. Measurements of advance of the active lee slope have been made at two points on this front over a period of six seasons: 1945–1946 to 1950–1951. Where the new dunes have overpassed the old (Station 3, Table 8; Pl. 15, fig. 2), average annual advance was 2.84 m; where progress falls short of the old (Station 4), 1.79 m. At both stations the rate increased notably through the last three seasons of record; this may or may not continue. Using the first three seasons only, the rates were 1.80 m and 1.03 m respectively. Averaging these, complete extinction of the stabilized dunes will require 5 centuries, but most of the task will have been accomplished in 300–400 years. Including the more rapid rate of recent seasons, the total time required is 300 years.

Recurrent outflow from Cleawox Lake and its results.—The extensive plant-covered area that makes so conspicuous an interruption in the zone of transverse ridges (Pl. 3, Locality 20, *B*; Pl. 19, fig. 2) is the result of occasional outflow from Cleawox Lake, which most of the time has no surface outlet. In series of years with unusually heavy rainfall it has discharged through a low place in the dune barrier and across the belt of transverse ridges. So small and short-lived a stream can hardly be responsible for planation of so extensive an area, but it can act as an effective barrier to sand moving southeastward before the summer wind by carrying away most of the material reaching its line of flow. The wind is thus free to bring about deflation of the area to leeward of the stream.

Twice during the last century and a half the lake has overflowed, and an extensive area has been deflated.[41] The first event is proved by an area north of the meadow where numerous dead pine trunks project from the expanse of transverse ridges and by a large spruce, overturned but in 1941 still living (Pl. 3, Locality 20, *C*). An incomplete core from this tree showed 128 rings, and this spot was therefore a deflation surface a moderate number of years before 1813. After disappearance of the surface stream the sand invading from the northwest obliterated the deflation surface, and killed all vegetation except a few spruces tall enough to keep their heads above the sand. The tree mentioned above had produced adventitious roots 2 m above its base, proving burial to at least that depth.

The second episode of surface outflow is so recent that only half of the resulting deflation surface has been reinvaded. North of the surviving meadow is a strip of transverse-ridge pattern thickly dotted with willow bushes that have so far survived burial (Pl. 3, Locality 20, *D*; Pl. 19, fig. 2). The northwestern edge of this area marks approximately the course of the temporary outlet stream across the zone of transverse ridges. Southeast of this barrier to invasion from the northwest, the summer wind gradually carried away the sand, and the deflated area extended itself southward

---

[41] Mr. C. O. Morgan reports that in consequence of the exceptionally heavy rains of the season 1955–1956 Cleawox Lake was again overflowing. No information is as yet available as to the effects of this overflow where it crosses the dune belt.

and southeastward. Vegetation quickly became established upon it. In 1941 the area was essentially a meadow, but willow bushes 1–2 m tall were scattered thickly over it, and a few pines and spruces up to 7 years old and even a few hemlock seedlings were present. Aerophotos taken in 1953 show that in 12 years the meadow had changed into a willow thicket, in which numerous thriving pines and spruces were doubtless present.

As long as the stream barrier remained there was no serious threat from windward, but when with decreasing precipitation it dried up, invasion began. Its manner was determined by the presence of resistant plants, mainly willow clumps. Sand accumulated around these with tongue hills pendent to leeward. Coalescence produced tongues of larger size which advanced over the meadow. As the sand deepened, interference by plants decreased to the point where establishment of the transverse-ridge pattern became possible.

Erosion of the older masses at the inner margin of the deflated area has continued; between 1940 and 1953 a strip 70–150 m wide was cut away. During these 13 years increase of area due to deflation along the inner margin and decrease due to invasion by new sand have been approximately in balance. It seems probable that invasion would have had the upper hand were it not for the introduction of a new factor—rapid development of the marram-grass foredune with its associated deflation strip, which has markedly decreased the supply of new sand. The ultimate result, barring new outflow from Cleawox Lake, may well be the firm establishment of forest here, with the chain of events that inevitably follows.

This minor episode is significant in that it demonstrates the rapidity of colonization by vegetation where a moist, stable deflation surface comes into being, the difficulty of maintenance of such vegetation where supply of new sand is abundant, and the potent effect of introduction of a new factor, in this case an exotic grass.

RÉSUMÉ AND DISCUSSION: REGION III

General setting.—The shore line between Sea Lion Point and Cape Arago, anchored at those headlands, is, and has been, a gentle, even curve because of homogeneity of the materials at the shore. Its position and perhaps its degree of concavity, however, have not been constant. The line at the time of the recent sea-level maximum is set by the wave-cut dune bluffs in Localities 21 and 22. Such bluffs, because of the large amount of sand that must be removed to accomplish a given unit of horizontal cutting, are resistant relative to the lower masses that border most of the shore, but not so resistant as to stand out as headlands. Rate of retreat of the high wave-cut bluffs thus determines the rate for the whole dune shore. The present shore line lies 100–400 m farther out and is thus at present free of control by the bluffs. It may be slightly less concave than formerly.

Distribution of sand along the coast.—The amount of sand incorporated in the dunes varies from place to place on the Coos Bay dune sheet. The greatest accumulations, including both stabilized and active masses, occur immediately to the south of the two principal rivers. The masses just south of the Umpqua in Locality 22 are greatest of all, and a traverse southward from this point demonstrates the effect of differences in volume of sand delivered at the beach upon what happens farther inland. Near the mouth of the Umpqua there must have been superabundance ever since the present active system began its march, for the oblique ridges extend to the littoral zone. Southward, with lessening supply, they recede, leaving behind a comparatively thin sheet of sand bearing the transverse-ridge pattern which, however, permits relatively rapid movement of sand across it to the zone of oblique ridges. Passing still farther southward into Locality 23, sand supply has been insufficient to maintain a continuous active sheet, and forest has developed.

Second in magnitude are the masses immediately south of the Siuslaw in Locality 20, and again there is decrease southward, extending almost to the Umpqua in Locality 21. It should be noted that extreme narrowness of the dune belt in the latter locality is a contributory cause of the small bulk of the dunes. Only at the Umpqua is there extra accumulation north of a river mouth, and this is limited to the parabola complex at the base of the peninsula.

Extra accumulation at the mouths of large rivers is proof of the importance of these as sources of supply. Decrease in dune mass with increasing distance shows that much of their contribution does not travel far along the coast. Location of extra accumulation almost entirely on the south sides of the rivers indicates that on this part of the coast the southward-flowing longshore current of summer is and has been much more effective than the northward-flowing current of winter.

Dune forms and their development.—Every dune form found on this coast, with the single exception of the beach-ridge system associated with progradation, occurs in optimum development on the Coos Bay dune sheet. The dominating type for the stabilized dunes is a massive precipitation ridge roughly parallel to the shore, in the production of which both summer and winter winds participate. The stabilized dunes, where there is sufficient breadth, show recessional ridges testifying to alternation of quiescence and activity during the phase of decline. Parabolas and parabola complexes occur and attain great size. They are, however, special features rather than dominating forms as in Region II.

In the active dunes the precipitation ridge is again the dominant structure, but in most places there is attached to it a series of massive oblique ridges, the whole constituting a system that moves inland as a unit. The oblique ridges are not everywhere equally developed, and degree of development is plainly correlated with degree of suitability in the conditions provided. The transverse-ridge system is represented in all localities, in greatest perfection in Locality 20.

History of the Coos Bay dune sheet.—The general inland movement of the dunes is closely bound to the latest period of submergence. In the terminal localities (19 and 23) three episodes of advance are evident. For the intervening coast the history may be brought into line by assuming that, due to local conditions, the second and third have merged. As in Region II, the advances are designated Episodes I, II, and III.

Episode I is represented in all localities by the stabilized masses that form the inner portion of the dune sheet. Recessional ridges indicate successive minor advances. The phase of declining activity is manifest also in remnant hills, which prove that ridgy masses representing still younger recessional ridges existed where there is now a sea of moving sand. The presence of such, clothed with mature climax forest, implies existence of a protecting strip of forested deflation surface to seaward. In

Locality 19 this still exists as the central plain. Changes in drainage and development of marginal lakes came to an end at the time of stabilization of the innermost, oldest ridges. As in Region II, stabilization of these early dunes was essentially complete before the sea had reached the ultimate limit of its transgression. This is proved by the slicing off of large parts of the parabola complexes north and south of the Umpqua River.

Episode II is represented in Locality 19 by the western ridge system; in Locality 23 the eastern active ridge system is the apparent counterpart. Deflation plains are associated with both and indicate a lengthy period of deficient sand supply.

Episode III is manifest in both terminal localities but in very different expression. In Locality 23 it is represented by the young precipitation-oblique-ridge system that borders the shore. In Locality 19 attack has been by erosion rather than burial; the outer plain has been cut up irregularly with formation of precipitation ridges and associated deflation surfaces that have quickly acquired forest cover. The processes here as in previous episodes in this locality reflect a persisting shortage of sand supply.

In the intervening three localities there is, aside from the inner strip of stabilized dunes, only a great wavelike mass of active sand, essentially a long precipitation-oblique-ridge system. There is a definite link between this system and Episode II in that the oblique-ridge series of Locality 22 is continued southward as the inner active series of Locality 23. There is in Locality 22 no sign of a system developed by a third advance. A surge of activity to match the latest one in the terminal localities is a reasonable inference; its effects have been obscured by continuity of abundant sand supply due principally to the Siuslaw and Umpqua Rivers. Development of a barrier forest has been impossible, and no new precipitation ridge has formed.

The final event in the history is the advent and rapid spread of marram grass, which, by establishing a barrier to inland transport of sand, ever increasing in effectiveness, must have a profound influence in shaping the future of the dunes.

There is confirmation in Region III of slight emergence after maximum advance of the sea in the forested wave-cut bluffs with wide beach in front of them in Localities 21 and 22.

RATE OF DUNE MOVEMENT IN REGION III

The rate of dune movement is useful in any estimate of the time element in dune history; it is also important in planning measures of dune control. It is an immensely variable quantity, ranging from the rapid progress of a small transverse ridge to the slow creep of a high slipface. For the most part, too, it is difficult to measure. The only situation where satisfactory quantitative data can be obtained is where an active slipface is invading a stabilized dune surface or new territory. Here the edge of the new sand is usually very definite. Fortunately such a situation is the most useful in time estimates and for planning of control measures. The series of six stations selected for measurement of rate of advance, all on the Coos Bay dune sheet, differ considerably in local conditions, but in combination they give an adequate picture of the general process. The study covered a period of 6 years (5 at Station 2), from September 1, 1945 to September 1, 1951. Measurements were made by Mr. C. O. Morgan of Winchester Bay, Oregon, on the first of each month, April to September. Total advance

TABLE 8.—*Rate of dune advance at six stations on the Coos Bay dune sheet*

Six seasons, Sept. 1, 1945–Sept. 1, 1951

	Locality 19		Locality 20		Locality 22		
	Sta. 1	Sta. 2	Sta. 3	Sta. 4	Sta. 5	Sta. 6	
Length of record, years	6	5	6	6	6	6	
Distance from shore, m	2300	4200	2000	2700	2100	2000	
Approx. height of slipface, m	10	10–15	25	10	. . . .	. . . .	
							Average Stations 1–4
Total advance, cm							
Sept.–March	137	36	312	234	160	66	180
April–Aug.	475	330	1389	841	876	234	759
Year	612	366	1701	1075	1036	300	938
Average per year, cm							
Sept.–March	23	7	52	39	27	11	30
April–Aug.	79	66	232	140	146	39	129
Year	102	73	284	179	173	50	160
Per cent of total, April–Aug.	77%	90%	82%	78%	84%	78%	81%

Description of stations:

1. Rejuvenated terminal ridge invading central plain; no access to receptive shore. (Pl. 3, Locality 19).

2. Rejuvenated terminal ridge invading older dunes near inner edge of dune sheet; no access to receptive shore. (Pl. 3, Locality 19).

3. High slipface at inner edge of dune sheet invading new territory which until recently supported high forest (Pl. 15, fig. 2), clear-cut one year before start of measurements; free access to receptive shore. (Pl. 3, Locality 20).

4. Slipface invading older dunes; free access to receptive shore. (Pl. 3, Locality 20).

5. Advancing inner point of major oblique ridge (*A-A* of Figure 7, Locality 22); no true slipface; free access to receptive shore. (Pl. 3, Locality 22).

6. Edge of sand in corridor *B-B* of Figure 7, Locality 22; gentle slope, no slipface; free access to receptive shore. (Pl. 3, Locality 22).

for the rainy season (September–March) was recorded on April 1. The results of the study are summarized in Table 8.

The factors that affect rate of advance are numerous and so closely interrelated that it is impossible to separate them completely. Comparison of data for the six stations does, however, bring out some useful facts and makes possible some tentative deductions. First of all, Stations 5 and 6 (Locality 22) must be separated from the others, since they possess no true slipfaces, and advance is highly irregular. They represent, respectively, the inner tip of a massive oblique ridge and the inner end of the adjoining corridor (*A-A* and *B-B*, Fig. 7). As noted in the section on the oblique-ridge system, most of the sand is swept from the corridors and travels along the ridges. Advance in the former thus naturally lags. The difference in measured rate between the two stations during the period of study is, however, too great to be applicable to their whole history.

The four remaining stations are comparable in that all have well-developed slipfaces. Three factors that must affect the rate of advance may be evaluated to some extent from the data: distance from shore with resulting decrease in wind effectiveness; access to receptive shore; height of slipface. As to the first there is a fairly satisfactory inverse relation: the rate at the station nearest the shore (Station 3) is four times that at the farthest (Station 2). The other two are intermediate in distance and in rate. Between rate of advance and access to receptive shore there is, so far as the data go, a clear relation: Stations 3 and 4, with free access, show a far higher rate than Stations 1 and 2, with none. With height of slipface, other things being equal, rate of advance should vary inversely. The data available, however, show no correlation at all. Station 3, with by far the highest slipface, had an advance far more rapid than the others, which, with comparable height of slipface, vary widely.

As is to be expected, the most rapid advance takes place during the relatively dry period April–August (77–90 per cent of the average total for the year). Whereas the southwesterly winter gales move enormous quantities of wet sand, it is principally the constant north-northwesterly wind of summer that slowly but steadily builds out the long slipfaces that are mainly responsible for eastward extension of the dune masses.

The average of 1.6 m based upon the four stations with well-developed slipfaces (Table 8, last column) is probably a fair estimate of annual advance of the dune front as a whole. By itself, however, it is useless for dating events in the past, since it covers only those portions of time when the front is in actual motion. There have been periods of no advance due to temporary stabilization, and there is also the time elapsed since stabilization of the innermost existing ridges. The rate of 1.6 m per year must therefore be the absolute maximum for long-time over-all advance. Application of this maximum rate to the widest part of the dune sheet (in Locality 19) demonstrates vividly the slowness of the advance; the time required to cover the 4400 m between the position of the present shore and the inner margin of the stabilized dunes is 2750 years plus periods of temporary stabilization plus the time since final stabilization.

An estimate of rate based upon a period extending almost a century into the past is possible through ring counts of living trees buried and partially exhumed in the advance of a terminal ridge (Pl. 20, fig. 3). A spruce in the general vicinity of Station 2 (Locality 19), 120 m back of the edge of the slipface, gave an age count of 160 years. Adding an arbitrary 20 years for the buried portion, the minimum average annual rate of sand advance from tree to present margin is .67 m. This tree after burial produced an adventitious root, the age of which close to the trunk was 57 years. Dividing distance by this gives 2.11 m as the maximum average annual advance. The actual rate must lie between these limits—as does also the rate determined by direct measurement. Another tree in the same vicinity, similarly treated, gave limiting rates of .90 m and 2.04 m. The figure from direct measurement is thus confirmed.

Qualitative information as to the nature and rate of change in recent dune history and some quasi-quantitative data may be derived from a series of photographs in Locality 23. In 1911 Mr. T. T. Munger of the Pacific Northwest Forest and Range Experiment Station, in the course of a reconnaissance study on the Coos Bay dune sheet, made the photograph reproduced in Figure 1A of Plate 21. The station was one of the remnant stabilized masses that stand isolated upon the incompletely reduced deflation plain associated with the eastern active ridge system (X on Pl. 3, Locality 23). The view is almost due north and includes a part of the deflation plain on the west and the ridge system on the east. The same station was occupied by the writer in 1933 and 1941; Figure 1, B of Plate 21 is from the photograph taken on the latter date.

Considerable change is apparent in distribution of dry sand on the deflation area, which is less significant than it seems. The 1911 picture was taken in early April when the water table was high; the 1941 picture was made in mid-September when the water was low and most of the surface covered by a thin sheet of drifting sand. Extensive changes occurred in the vegetation cover. The pine forest in the middle ground, represented in 1911 by scattered pioneer trees, had by 1941 extended itself well beyond the middle of the picture, and most of this development had taken place before 1933. The most distant forest patch in the center increased in extent and height in its inner portion while the seaward edge was undergoing destruction. Two small forest remnants visible near the left edge of the 1911 picture were completely destroyed before 1933.

The photographs also make possible a rough approximation of the rate of eastward shift of the eastern active ridge system measured at its windward margin. That there has been a definite change is obvious from the photographs. By a crude process of triangulation, utilizing the pictures of Figure 1 of Plate 21 and an aerophoto made in 1941, with points that did not change perceptibly in the interval between pictures as controls, it was estimated that a certain point on the windward margin—the apex of the most distant projection—shifted 48 m in 30 years, which gives an average rate of 1.6 m per year. This again confirms the average obtained by direct measurements of slipface advance, though the exact correspondence is of course a coincidence.

Comparison of the two sets of aerophotos of Localities 20, 21, and 22 made in 1940 and 1953 reveals many changes of small magnitude. Some are significant and are considered where they are applicable.

REGION IV: SOUTHERN OREGON
GENERAL FEATURES

Region IV comprises all the dune localities occurring between Cape Arago and the California boundary; the only ones of material importance lie north of Cape Blanco. Nowhere are the dunes of great height or bulk, but they are no less significant on that account. Their considerable inland extension in certain parts is due to the lowness, flatness, and breadth of the surface on which they lie.

LOCALITY 24: COQUILLE RIVER NORTH

Extent.—The dune belt (Pl. 4, Locality 24) extends from the Coquille River north to Whisky Run, a distance of 7.5 km exclusive of the spit at the river mouth, which adds 2.5 km. Its breadth is 1.2–2 km.

Substratum.—From the north end at Whisky Run south to Cut Creek the dunes rest upon a terrace surface bounded by a cliff that rises 15–30 m above the beach. The cliff ends abruptly at Cut Creek; southward the substratum surface is below sea level at the shore. Behind the dunes the terrace surface rises in steps; the highest level stands at more than 150 m (Griggs, 1945).

Dune-sand mantle.—There are three overlapping sheets of dune sand. The two oldest have been completely stabilized, though they differ greatly in stage of vegetational development; the youngest is active. All have precipitation ridges remarkably regular and free from lobation.

The oldest sheet is unbroken all the way from the Coquille River to Whisky Run, which has set a limit to northward advance. The portion north of Cut Creek has had a considerable part sliced away by the sea, and the resulting cliff has deprived it of its source of supply. The sheet consists of a very regular and continuous precipitation ridge with steep lee slope and gentle windward slope hummocky from the effects of final saucer-blowout activity, and a broad deflation plain. North of Cut Creek the plain extends to the cliff; southward it has been invaded by the younger sheets.

Over almost the entire extent of the oldest sheet the forest has been clear-cut; it is the only considerable area of dunes where this has occurred. One fair-sized body remains, and this and scattered small patches indicate that the original forest was made up of large trees and that it had attained climax or near-climax status. The breadth of the plain and its almost complete reduction to deflation base indicate that a long period of comparative quiescence elapsed before the second invasion. It was during this period that a lake of considerable size, impounded behind the dunes, of which Round Lake is probably a remnant, broke through the barrier of the precipitation ridge, perhaps at a time of flood, and cut a sharp ravine through dune sand and substratum on its way to the sea. The stream that flows in it is Cut Creek.

The second invasion nowhere approached the full extent of the first. The main existing body, whose precipitation ridge lies 1–1.5 km east of the beach, is tributary to the portion of the shore south of Cut Creek, where receptivity has been retained. This mass in its northward extension encountered an obstacle in the newly formed Cut Creek, just as happened in the first invasion at Whisky Run. The precipitation ridge is similar in magnitude to that of the earliest sheet. The deflation plain, though flat and completely stabilized, is not densely forested; clumps of open-grown trees are scattered over a meadowlike surface. A prominent fragment of precipitation ridge occurs at the edge of the cliff just south of Whisky Run; it is comparable to the precipitation ridge south of Cut Creek and may indicate a contemporaneous structure almost all of which has been cut away.

The third sheet is in contact with receptive shore over its whole length. Its precipitation ridge is active all the way from the Coquille River to Cut Creek, which here again forms a barrier to northward extension, carrying out to sea the sliding sand. The active sheet has taken over most of the area of the second, and at the north it has in places overpassed the latter's precipitation ridge and is invading the deflation plain of the first sheet. There is a typical active slipface continuous except at the north end. Advance of the ridge has been rapid; at the north end groups of trees survive more than 300 m behind the slipface, and trees are being buried all along the line. Next to the slope the deflation plain is thinly covered with moving sand; near the shore, where the water table is close to the surface, there is much low vegetation. Succession here, already begun, will lead to pine and spruce forest, which will cut off the supply of new sand from the active precipitation ridge. Final stabilization of the active sand sheet will result in approximate duplication of the features of the second.

LOCALITY 25: COQUILLE RIVER SOUTH

Extent.—Locality 25 extends from the Coquille River south to Fourmile Creek, a distance of 13 km (Pl. 4). It divides naturally into five subunits. The first four are minor but display points of interest; the fifth is of major importance.

Substratum.—The dunes rest upon the terrace surface which is here very wide (Griggs, 1945). At Coquille Point and for a distance of 4 km south the terrace is bounded by a cliff less than 30 m high. A flock of rocky islets and stacks, some retaining remnants of the terrace surface, stand off the point. Over the southern 7 km the substratum is below sea level at the shore and little above it at the inner edge of the dunes.

Dune-sand mantle.—Subunits *A* and *B* are mere remnants completely cut off from supply by the cliff. Subunit *C* is similar except that its southern part has some access to receptive shore and is therefore more active. All three have inner stabilized strips that are being invaded by active sand. In subunit *D* the stabilized dunes have been almost completely destroyed, but there are outcrops of the older surface behind the low advancing slipface. Bradley Lake is due to damming of China Creek by the early dunes. An active slipface descends today to its lower end.

At Twomile Creek, the northern boundary of subunit *E*, the dune belt abruptly doubles in width. The sharp offset to the east is due to the limit imposed upon northward extension by the creek. Offsets similarly caused are seen at the northern boundaries of subunits *B*, *C*, and *D*. The main movement of sand in the early history was plainly from the southwest.

The substratum upon which the dunes of subunit *E* rest is but slightly above sea level; the surface of marginal Laurel Lake stands at only 4 m. Here, as in Locality 24, there have been three successive invasions, each represented by a sheet of sand bounded by a precipitation ridge. The oldest survives over a distance of 2.5 km at the north end and in a group of remnant masses at the south that have successfully resisted the two later invasions. Some of these, a considerable distance to seaward, are more than 30 m high. Stabilization of the old surfaces has reached completion, and the forest on them has climax or near-climax status.

The second sheet differs from its counterpart in Locality 24 in having retained to the present a state of vigorous activity. Its precipitation ridge is everywhere invading the deflation plain of the oldest sheet, and southward it has overpassed that sheet completely and is entering new ground. Living trees partially buried, a considerable distance behind the slipface, show that advance is rapid. The deflation plain exhibits all stages of vegetational development: bare sand, pioneers, a fairly continuous belt of pine forest, and at the north, about to be overwhelmed, a narrow strip of near-climax forest, which suggests that much of the area buried by the third advance had reached that state.

The third advance is marked by an active precipitation ridge similar to that of the second. Its almost unbroken slipface is invading the deflation plain of the second sheet over a distance of 3 km, and rapid advance is indicated by living trees projecting from the sand 100–150 m behind it. Several remnant masses from the first sheet, left behind in the advance of the second, have again been by-passed by the third. The deflation plain is very flat, and the only vegetation present is of the pioneering stage;

pine forest has nowhere been established. There is everywhere contact with receptive shore. At the outer edge is a fairly definite foredune zone made up of marram-grass hillocks.

LOCALITY 26: FOURMILE CREEK[42]

Extent.—The locality is continuous with the last, extending from Fourmile Creek south 13 km to Floras Lake (Pl. 4, Locality 26).

Substratum.—The 2-km-wide low-lying terrace of Locality 25 continues southward through Locality 26 to Floras Lake, south of which cliffs of Tertiary sandstone begin abruptly and possibly indicate a higher terrace level. The terrace surface between Fourmile Creek and Crooks Lake,[43] and at the extreme south end just north of Floras Lake, though very low, is still above the water table at the inner edge of the dunes. The remainder is flat and swampy behind the dunes, with numerous ponds, and barely above sea level. Crooks Lake and New Lake lie in shallow sags in the terrace surface, not in drowned valleys, and their open connection with the lagoon behind the beach ridge shows that they are almost at sea level. Floras Lake, separated from the sea merely by a beach ridge and hardly higher, lies partly on the lower surface and partly in ravines cut into the more elevated mass south of the lake. Nowhere within the dune belt is the substratum exposed. It is below sea level at the shore line, and therefore the dunes have unbroken access to receptive shore.

Dune-sand mantle.—Only two sand sheets are present: a stabilized inner one and an active outer one. Division into subunits is essential to clear description.

The stabilized dunes between Fourmile Creek and Crooks Lake (subunit *A*) cannot be mapped with exactness in all parts. Three precipitation ridges are, however, plain; all of them have steep, narrow windward slopes, indicating contraction as they advanced owing to meagerness of sand supply. They do not, apparently, represent separate major episodes. Southward the complex is transformed into a series of narrow overlapping parabolas controlled by the summer wind. A section in a ditch shows that at one point at least the dune sand rests upon peat. The last two parabolas have permanent ponds and areas of bog in their troughs—a situation unique for the whole coast. The peat deposits in them have a depth of at least 1.2 m. Height of the southernmost parabola above the surface of Crooks Lake, by aneroid, is 14.5 m; of the pond within its walls, 1.8 m. The active sheet has a precipitation ridge that is invading the older dunes in a rather feeble manner. Its deflation plain presents a mosaic of wet and dry, vegetated and bare areas.

The type of dune structure found in subunits *B* and *C*, both stabilized and active, differs profoundly from that characteristic of subunit *A* and the localities farther north. In place of the massive regular precipitation ridge is a connected series of slender tongues, various in length, strictly aligned with the summer wind. The type has been already described, and as a minor feature has been encountered in a number

---

[42] The field work in this locality was carried out by Dr. John W. Marr in June, 1952, and Dr. Quentin D. Clarkson in August, 1954.

[43] This name follows the Port Orford sheet of 1897–1898, U. S. Geol. Surv., the only available map. The name used by local residents is Crofts Lake.

of places. Its manner of development here, as demonstrated by the active system, is as follows:

The low, very flat, for the most part wet substratum supports a mixed plant growth: bushes and trees, singly and in clumps, scattered over an expanse of low herbaceous vegetation. Tongue hills developed from mounds tied to the woody plants coalesce into the large tongues that constitute the moving front. Sand movement on these low masses is possible only in summer, and there is thus no counter action to disturb the summer-wind pattern. Supply from the shore is exceedingly meager. If it were abundant, a sheet of dry sand bearing the transverse-ridge pattern would spread inland behind the sand-tongue system and kill the vegetation, as in Locality 20. Meager sand supply in combination with a particular vegetation type thus determines the dune form.

Exactly the same forms and processes have characterized the earlier history as far back as it is accessible. On the low, flat expanse that lies to landward of the active system there are in subunits B and C strips of slightly higher ground that by form and alignment are unmistakably ancient sand tongues like those of the present. In the course of centuries their contours have become greatly softened, and in part their outlines are masked by vegetation.

Subunit D is of small consequence; it consists of a mere fringe of dunes which, however, like the others, is divided into stabilized and active strips.

DISCUSSION: LOCALITIES 24–26

This series of localities is second to the Coos Bay dune sheet in total length and in length of receptive shore: 37 km and 29 km respectively. It differs in the presence of two areas of perched dunes on cliffed terraces. These show that the dune belt here, as in localities farther north, has been sliced by the advancing sea. The amount of sand embodied is far less per unit of shore frontage than in the Coos Bay dune sheet. One cause probably lies in the fact that it is bounded by two very prominent headlands—Cape Arago on the north and Cape Blanco on the south. Both must to some extent direct the longshore currents out to sea; the latter marks the most radical change of trend on the whole Washington-Oregon coast. Only one fair-sized river, the Coquille, enters the sea between them; the dunes north of it (Locality 24) doubtless benefit from the sand it carries. Southward drift is hindered by Coquille Point, and there is no receptive shore immediately adjacent. The maximum bulk of sand in this direction therefore lies some distance from the river, between Twomile Creek and Crooks Lake. At the latter point the amount drops off abruptly; at Floras Creek there is almost none.

The histories in the two areas of best development—Localities 24 and 25E—are similar. Three major dune advances appear in both. The first was followed by a long period of quiescence, shown by the almost completely reduced deflation plains and, in Locality 25, the by-passed remnants standing far to seaward. The interval of quiescence following the second advance, judging from incomplete vegetation development in Locality 24 and continuing activity in Locality 25, was shorter. The present, third advance seems to be catching up with the second in both localities.

In the remaining part of Locality 25 and in Locality 26 there are only an inner thoroughly stabilized system and an outer active one. The inner is undoubtedly to be correlated with the first advance in the series of three; the outer must therefore combine the second and third. Episodes I, II, and III appear here as in the regions to the north.

LOCALITY 27: SIXES RIVER

This is an unimportant body of dune sand just north of Cape Blanco on the flat at the mouth of Sixes River (Pl. 1). There is a small-scale active precipitation ridge and deflation plain, and a narrow tongue of sand ascends the 30-m bluff and extends a short distance beyond it on the terrace top.

LOCALITIES SOUTH OF CAPE BLANCO

General features.—The gentle curve of the shore line that begins at Cape Flattery, concave seaward, its southern half trending a little west of south, ends at Cape Blanco (Pl. 1). Thence the general trend is south-southeast to the California boundary. The upwarped, cliffed terrace continues past Cape Blanco to Port Orford. Beyond, the mountain front, higher than northward, is at the shore. Terrace remnants are present here and there, but their margins are cliffed; everywhere the shore is bold and rocky and irregular in detail. In view of the almost complete absence of receptive shore it is not surprising that dunes are scarce. Even at the Rogue River, which delivers a heavy load of sediment, there are no dunes of consequence.

Locality 28: Elk River.—Elk River crosses the terrace between Cape Blanco and Port Orford. Perched upon the bluffs south of the river is a narrow strip of dunes, a remnant of a much larger mass that early in the period of submergence had access to receptive shore. All that remains is a pair of stabilized ridges undergoing active erosion, which has probably been accelerated by timber cutting and grazing. A large area of terrace top has been stripped completely bare (Pl. 21, fig. 2). At the time of my visit the northerly summer wind was blowing at gale strength almost parallel to the shore. The southward-flowing longshore current was extremely active and made the water very turbid. With no lodgment area other than the narrow beach, most of the sediment must sweep past The Heads and out into deep water. Sand blew along the beach with terrific velocity and was lifted even from wet surfaces; a small amount ascended by way of gullies to the terrace top.

Locality 29: Euchre Creek.—A small flat at the mouth of the creek gives lodgment, and a minor dune mass, consisting of an active precipitation ridge invading forest, has developed upon it.

Locality 30: Pistol River.—The dune mass here is by far the most considerable of those south of Cape Blanco; it is notable also for the vigor of its recent activity. The axis of the dune mass indicates that the summer wind has always been in control. Two major advances are apparent. The first is represented by a triangular stabilized mass pointing south-southeast. On the active sand of the second advance the dominating features are widely spaced ridges driven straight ahead by the summer wind. On the central sector of the front a successful effort has been made to stop the advance that was threatening to overwhelm a farm. No serious attempt at control has been made on the seaward sector, and advance continued until it reached a stream, which as usual brought to a halt the rapid progress of the dune.

REGION I: COLUMBIA RIVER
GENERAL FEATURES

The major coastal features north of Tillamook Head are the estuary of the Columbia River and the two wide, shallow indentations, Willapa Bay and Grays Harbor (Pl. 1). The bays have for a long time acted as settling basins and are now well filled with sediment. The three localities north of the Columbia (Pl. 5) make a continuous strip 90 km long, broken only at the mouths of the bays, and comprising forelands where in contact with the mountain front and peninsulas (too broad and complex to be called bars or spits) outside the water bodies. Locality 4, south of the Columbia, is mainly an attached foreland.

LOCALITIES NORTH OF THE COLUMBIA RIVER

Locality 3: Willapa Bay.—This is considered first because in it the characteristic forms are best developed. The peninsula outside Willapa Bay and Shoalwater Bay is built mainly of parallel beach ridges (Pl. 5, Locality 3; Pl. 21, fig. 3). These are for the most part low, attaining in general a height above sea level of 6–12 m. So weak in expression are they that reconstruction of the ridge pattern from aerophotos depends mainly upon certain features of the forest pattern. A narrow strip of trees represents a single narrow ridge rising slightly above the bog level; a broad belt of forest indicates a broad ridge or a group in virtual contact. The fragmentary reconstruction of Plate 5, Locality 3 is intended to portray only the general pattern.

Between the ridges or groups are linear areas of bog and numerous elongated lakes; the latter are remnants of much larger water bodies now mostly filled with peat. These lie very close to sea level; two bench marks in troughs give altitudes of 1.5 and 1.8 m. The bottoms of some of these basins must quite certainly lie below sea level.

Over the southern half of the peninsula—from Klipsan Beach to the end—the parallel-ridge pattern extends uniformly to the ocean shore. At Klipsan Beach begins a ridge (*A*, Pl. 5, Locality 3), much more abrupt than the gentle swells of the general pattern, that bounds the forested area on the west all the way to its northern extremity. At the south it is completely stabilized. Erosion is first apparent in the vicinity of Ocean Park; it increases northward. Trough blowouts appear oriented with the summer winds; these merge into a continuous active strip with small remnants left behind. Finally no remnants survive; the ridge is invading the forest, and scattered living trees project from its windward slope. Outside it is a strip of open sand, narrow at the south and expanding to 800 m at its northern end. A foredune lies between this and the beach. A spit almost bare of vegetation extends 4 km beyond the apex of the peninsula proper.

On the bayward side of the peninsula, east of the parallel-ridge system, is a series of ridge segments, not straight nor regular, that may reasonably be connected in a single sinuous line. Altitudes range for the most part from 6 to 12 m, but on one segment a height of 25 m is attained—the highest point on the peninsula. Next to the bay is a low strip that merges with the tidal flats.

At the southern end of the peninsula is an extensive bog area—"Cranberry Marsh" —between the parallel-ridge system and the mountain front. Borings made by Dachnowski-Stokes (1936) and Hansen (1944; 1947) give depths of peat as 1.7 m and 2.8 m. The mineral substratum here lies close to sea level, perhaps below.

Locality 2: Grays Harbor South.—This locality consists of a foreland attached to the mountain mass between Willapa Bay and Grays Harbor and a northward-pointing peninsula outside the latter. In its general features it closely resembles Locality 3. Parallel ridges are definitely present on the peninsula; they are recorded in field notes and indicated by a forest pattern. As in the northern half of Locality 3 the stabilized strip is being invaded by an active ridge (*A*, Pl. 5, Locality 2) that here extends the entire distance. From Grayland south, where settlements lie close behind, there has been much artificial stabilization. Outside the active ridge is a counterpart to the sandy strip in Locality 3; it is partly bare and partly covered with salt rush and other low vegetation. Finally there is a continuous but rather poorly defined foredune. On the bayward side there is no distinguishable counterpart to the irregular ridge of Locality 3. There is, however, a low-lying strip that merges with the tidal flats on the peninsula and with an elongated area next to the mountain front, originally bog or swamp, now occupied by cranberry farms. A boring by Hansen (1944; 1947) gave a depth to substratum of 2.1 m, which is very close to sea level. At the inner margin of the foreland is an interrupted bluff that truncates the mountain spurs; where the mountain front recedes along the shore of Grays Harbor there is no such feature.

Locality 1: Grays Harbor North.—In its arrangement of parts this is the reverse of Locality 2: its northern portion is a very narrow foreland tapering off at Copalis Head, its southern a southward-pointing peninsula facing its corresponding feature in Locality 2. Structurally it is in essential agreement with the localities to the south. Along the bayward edge of the peninsula is a ridge, not quite straight, which may correspond to the irregular inner ridge of Locality 3. Next westward is a strip with parallel ridges, and bogs and lakes in the troughs between them. The ridges are in places distinguishable on aerophotos, but for the most part their trends must be inferred from the forest pattern, and in Duck Lake from lines of trees whose bases were submerged when the photos were made. Where they join the bayshore ridge their trend is discordant with it, diverging somewhat to seaward.

This older strip is bounded on the west by a relatively abrupt ridge, (*A*, Pl. 5, Locality 1) that plainly corresponds to the similar feature in Localities 2 and 3. At the southern end of the peninsula it extends to the water's edge of Grays Harbor, curving inward and cutting off the ridges of the older strip at an acute angle. Parts of it are moderately active, eroding on the outer face and invading the forest on the inner.

The younger strip outside ridge *A* is of far greater extent than in the other localities; it occupies, in fact, at least three-fourths of the peninsula. It possesses the parallel-ridge pattern, and there are linear ponds in the troughs. The ridges, which are very subdued, increase in number and in distance apart southward; they curve inward as they approach the end of the peninsula, parallel to ridge *A* but with increasing convexity. There are trees, singly or in groves, on the older portion, but no continuous forest. The vegetation is principally herbaceous, and trends of ridges are indicated by the thin plant cover on their crests. Beyond the last of this series is a thin foredune that extends all the way from Point Brown to Copalis Head.

LOCALITY 4: CLATSOP PLAINS

General features.—Locality 4, on the south side of the Columbia, extends from the river mouth southward 30 km, and ends abruptly at the rocky mass of Tillamook Head (Pl. 1). Although its ridge system is of the same general type as those north of the river, it differs from them in being attached to the upland for most of its length and in greater complexity in structure and in development. A tracing from a mosaic is presented in Plate 6.

Certain features of the locality are so striking that they attracted the attention of the earliest visitors. Lewis and Clark noted the ridges (Lewis and Clark, ed. Thwaites, 1905, p. 271, 320), and J. D. Dana, geologist of the Wilkes Expedition of 1838–1842 (Dana, 1849, p. 667–668), wrote a surprisingly adequate account of them. In more recent years Diller (1895–1896) and W. D. Smith (1933) have described them and offered suggestions as to their mode of origin. Still more recently members of the U. S. Soil Conservation Service, in connection with their program of artificial stabilization of the dunes, have discussed the development of the ridges (Rowalt, 1936; McLaughlin, 1939; McLaughlin and Brown, 1942; Arnst, 1942a; 1942b). Because of sharper relief and lesser amount of forest cover, study in this locality has been more rewarding, both in the field and from aerophotos, than in the localities north of the Columbia.

The margin of the upland behind the Clatsop Plains, taken as a whole, describes a gentle, regular curve which doubtless marks a coastal bluff developed at a period of high sea level antedating initiation of progradation. The site of Cullaby Lake was a broad indentation. The substratum upon which the present sand formation rests is presumably a terrace platform in front of this bluff.

Building of the Clatsop Plains can be divided into three stages of progradation, defined today by three groups of ridges.[44] The dashed portions of the lines representing ridge crests in Plate 6 indicate uncertainty. For Stage I this is due to actual breaks in continuity. The segments cannot be linked with absolute certainty, but those in line must be very close in time of origin, and joining them seems justified. In Stage III, where disturbance has been severe during the last century, uncertainty applies to the exact location of the original ridge crests, not to their existence. In the ridges of Stage II there are no gaps, and disturbance has been insignificant.

Stage I (Ridges 1–2c).—There is evidence, somewhat vague, that progradation began with a short bay bar in front of Cullaby Lake (A, Pl. 22, fig. 1). The oldest extended ridge is number 1 of Plate 6 and stands about 300–500 m seaward of the upland margin. It is broken into segments which are for the most part 6–12 m in height. Where the margin of the upland swings to the east, the ridge continues straight northward. The land surface between it and the upland is very slightly above sea level.

Ridge 2 at its southern end lies near ridge 1, but northward it diverges to the west and divides into two ridges, designated 2a and 2b. The latter, diverging still farther,

---

[44] These are not correlatives of the three "episodes" of advance noted for localities of Region III, since the first of the latter antedates the maximum of sea advance, while the present three all postdate it. Neither is it possible to match any feature with the ridge *A* of Localities 1–3.

divides again, and gives rise to 2c. Ridge 2b extends almost or quite to the tip of the Point Adams peninsula. Ridge 2 in its southern part (B, Pl. 22, fig. 1) is narrow, interrupted, and low, and nowhere rises much more than 6 m above tide. Its three branches increase in massiveness northward, and each one culminates near its northern terminus in a high point of more than 24 m, beyond which there is gradual descent. The crests of these three branches are somewhat sinuous, and their surfaces are hummocky. The three interridge areas bounded by 1 and 2c and the lands on both sides of 2b at its northern end are very low. There are extensive areas of swamp and bog forest, which in places take the form of strips alternating with minor ridges. Ponds and slender lakes are numerous, and some of the latter are of considerable length.

The history during Stage I seems to have been as follows. Just before progradation began, the mouth of the Columbia River, bounded on the southeast by the upland east of the Skipanon River and on the northwest by Cape Disappointment, was 16 km wide. Outward flow of the river spread its bed load fanwise. The inevitable shoaling was apparently most pronounced at the southern side of the river mouth, perhaps because of slackening of the current in the lee of Smith Point, where Astoria now stands, and here there developed a northward-projecting spit. Extension of this structure was accompanied by seaward progradation. Ridge after ridge appeared, of various magnitudes and at various spatial intervals. The smaller ones, closely spaced, were ordinary beach ridges. Where a ridge has behind it a wide strip of bog or a considerable lake, origin as an offshore bar seems indicated. Rapid extension of shoaling would favor this process. As new ridges came into being they extended themselves progressively farther northward. The initial spit was gradually transformed into a broad peninsula that found its final limit of growth at Point Adams, presumably when coastal and fluvial forces attained a state of balance.

The massive diverging ridges at the north seem to have acquired their present bulk and irregularity during brief interruptions in the progress of progradation. The combined attack of surf and wind upon regular ridges already established moved their substance inland. Materials from several may have mingled to produce a massive structure, still parallel to the shore, but with the hummocky blowout relief characteristically developed under such conditions. Convergence and decreasing mass of the ridges southward is doubtless related to increasing distance from the source of supply.

Stage II (Ridges 3–5b).—The transition from Stage I to Stage II is marked by an abrupt change in character of the ridges; those of the latter stage have often attracted attention because of the striking regularity and continuity of their gently curving crests (Pl. 22, fig. 1). They are for the most part narrow and steep-sided and resemble railroad embankments. The only surface irregularities are shallow furrows that cross the crests obliquely, trending with the southwest winter winds. Recent disturbance has scarred them but slightly. They are for the most part unforested, and this condition is quite certainly natural since Lewis and Clark (1905, p. 271) use the expression "open ridgey prairie" and Dana (1849, p. 667–668) speaks of "the prairie plain", and "luxuriant growth of grass" a considerable distance back from the shore.[45]

Stage II at its southern end comprises three ridges (C, D, E, Pl. 22, fig. 1), each of which divides northward into two. There is almost no divergence; the branches of a pair are strictly parallel and close together, so that in places they might fairly be considered as single double-crested ridges. The northern extremities all end abruptly against the outermost ridge of Stage I, and make an acute angle with it, each one at a point farther north than the next older. Because of the close parallelism of the ridges, the strip is uniform in width except for reduction brought about by the successive dropping out of the older ridges northward. The intervals between the ridges are at high levels—almost all above 6 m—and average elevation of the whole strip is thus significantly greater than in the area of Stage I.

In the history of Stage II the facts are plain, but the underlying causes, comprising the forces inherent in river, sea, and wind, are obscure, perhaps undiscoverable. With cessation of northward extension at Point Adams, seaward progradation on the peninsula slackened or ceased. At about the same time there was conspicuous renewal of progradation farther south with the building of the ridges of Stage II, which gradually filled in the concavity of the shore line. That the sand was brought mainly by the southward-flowing littoral current is indicated by the doubling of the ridges at the north and their decrease in bulk southward. This current operates during the summer, when the beach sand is driest and dune grass is most effective in precipitating it. The mass of Tillamook Head, moreover, deflects seaward the northward-flowing current of winter.

There was here no building of offshore bars. Ridge was piled against ridge, so that a considerable depth of deposit was constantly maintained. There were, however, variations in rate due to changes in conditions at the shore, which may have included fluctuations in sand supply, in wind direction and velocity, and possibly slight changes in sea level. Progradation was never rapid. Steady, uninterrupted building out produced a deposit with generally level surface marked by discontinuous traces of minor ridge crests. These make up the interridge strips of today. A brief halt in general progradation gave opportunity for bringing of an extra supply of sand to the line of the shore and building of a high, massive, continuous ridge just behind that line. Throughout the history of Stage II there has been no serious attack by surf, which would inevitably have destroyed the perfect regularity of the ridges, as it did in Stage I.

Stage III. (Ridges 6–9b).—The area of Stage III is not so homogeneous as those of the preceding two; it is for the most part a unit of convenience. It extends the whole distance between the mass of Tillamook Head and Point Adams with an

---

[45] Dune grass (*Elymus arenarius* L. var. *villosus* Mey.) was certainly abundant near the shore. As to the species making up the "prairie" farther inland, Mr. R. L. Brown of the U. S. Soil Conservation Service (Personal communication) thinks that the most important were reed grass (*Calamagrostis inexpansa* Gray), hair grass (*Deschampsia caespitosa* (L.) Beauv.), blue wild rye (*Elymus glaucus* Buckl.), fescue (*Festuca rubra* L.), and bent grass (*Agrostis* spp.).

average width of about 1 km. The principal features are an inner fairly level strip and a pair of massive ridges outside.

For the inner strip the processes were a direct continuation of those in the adjoining areas of Stages I and II. Southward, bordering Stage II, the surface is relatively high. Progradation continued here after the manner of the older interridge strips— beach ridges piled one against another, producing a surface pattern of dim parallel crests of which a few were more pronounced; the most conspicuous was ridge 6 (F, Pl. 22, fig. 1). The strip thus characterized is 600 m wide from Gearhart to Sunset Lake; beyond, it becomes narrower, and the pattern is partly obscured by recent disturbance. At the north, where the strip adjoins Stage I, the manner of progradation again followed the course already set in this area: low ridges, some widely spaced (7, 8), with bogs, ponds, and lakes between them, indicate origin of some as offshore bars.

The two outermost ridges (G, Pl. 22, fig. 1), which apparently merge near the south end, have suffered severe disturbance since the advent of the white population. They were originally as massive as any in the entire area, as both are more than 20 m high in most of their length; several points are above 25 m. The crests quite certainly were somewhat sinuous and their surfaces hummocky like those of ridges 2a–2c, and their formation may have been similar. Development of irregularity in this way is quite distinct from the recent disturbance caused by man. The former is initiated at the shore and gradually works inland, whereas the latter is caused by breaking of the turf in many places at once over the entire surface, and is far more likely to result in quick and widespread destruction. Ridge 9b is close to the beach. Initiation of a new ridge in front of it through precipitation of sand by dune grass (Steele, 1940, picture on p. 43) brings the history to date.

The northern and southern parts of the area have throughout their history consistently maintained their differing modes of progradation. In the north, near the river mouth, where outward-flowing currents have been dominant and sand supply thus abundant, outbuilding has been carried farther than in the south; the prograded strip is twice as wide. The general level has remained low except for a few massive ridges that probably owe their bulk to interruptions in progradation. The offshore bar has been an important element in the process. In the south, farther from the river, with a lesser supply of sand, the littoral current has been the dominating agent, favoring production of numerous closely set beach ridges and a much greater average height of surface. Building of the outermost pair of ridges seems to have brought uniformity of process to the whole extent of shore.

Post-jetty history.—Before 1885, when construction of the south jetty began, there were extensive shoal areas beyond Point Adams, but no land. By 1902 Clatsop Spit had attained approximately its present form and size (U. S. Army Corps of Engineers, Portland District, personal communication), and a strip of newly deposited sand attached to it extended several km south along the seaward side of the Point Adams peninsula; this is now 700 m wide at the north and gradually narrows until its outer edge meets the old shore line (McLaughlin and Brown, 1942). Outbuilding of the shore has here been too rapid to permit formation of beach ridges stabilized by vegetation; most of the expanse of sand is bare.

HISTORY IN REGION I

The Grays Harbor and Willapa Bay re-entrants are very wide valleys, close together, cut in weak rocks across a broad foreland during the last grand period of emergence. The two valleys may well have merged with each other west of the present line of the coast, and perhaps also with that of the Columbia, to form a broad lowland transecting the coastal plain. In the early stages of submergence, a long bay bar may have extended across the seaward end of this broad valley with, of course, openings for the outflowing waters. The bar moved inward as submergence progressed. When the sea reached Cape Disappointment and the mountain mass between Grays Harbor and Willapa Bay the bar was cut into three segments. With further advance of the sea these continued their inland migration in step with recession of the bluffs that bounded them; they doubtless bore minor dunes subject to constant destruction and re-formation. Nowhere were great dune masses driven inland; the principal reason was lack of receptive shore. A bar may receive much sand from the waves, but, once ashore, there is nowhere for it to go but into the bay behind. The remainder of the frontage was unreceptive cliff.

At the maximum of sea advance there were wave-cut cliffs at the salient of Cape Disappointment, and bluffs between Willapa Bay and Grays Harbor, north of the latter, and between the Columbia and Tillamook Head. Narrow bars, probably bearing low dunes, stretched from headland to headland across the two bays. Remnants of the dunes should have survived, and these seem to be embodied in the nonlinear ridges that lie next to the bay shore in Localities 1 and 3.

With approximately constant sea level or slight lowering came a complete reversal in process: inland migration of the bars was succeeded by progradation.

North of the Columbia the course of events has been relatively simple. Starting at the line of farthest inland advance, formation of successive beach ridges converted the narrow bars with their unstable dunes to thoroughly stabilized, almost completely forested peninsulas, which increased constantly in width. Spacing of the ridges was not uniform. Certain rather wide strips of upland seem to represent groups of closely placed ridges. It appears that at times an offshore bar would form, holding behind it a lagoon which became an elongated lake with bottom below sea level; this finally was filled partially or completely with peat. Where the strip is a foreland rather than a peninsula the first progradational structure seems to have been an offshore bar. Between it and the mountain front in Localities 2 and 3 there is today a broad zone of peat land.

In the southern half of Locality 3 progradation by ridge building has gone on without significant interruption to the present. Northward, all the rest of the way to the end of Locality 1 there is evidence of a very definite interruption. The ridge designated A in the three localities, with its eroding seaward slope, its slipfaces invading the forest, and in Locality 1 its truncation of the older, true beach ridges, proves that at a fairly recent time the sea advanced against the land and pushed the shore back a short distance. Progradation began again. The new strip varies in width. Where it is narrow, beach ridges are not distinguishable; where it is broader, there are two to several.

South of the Columbia (Locality 4), the course of progradation has been complex; description and history have been combined in an earlier section.

EARLIER CYCLE OF DUNE DEVELOPMENT

On the coast of Oregon south of Tillamook Head the dunes of recent time acquired their essential character during the latest grand period of submergence. There is abundant evidence that a similar history of dune development accompanied an earlier period of submergence when the penetration of the land was somewhat greater than during the latest one. This evidence resides in bodies of eolian sand that make a minor but significant portion of the unconsolidated sediments which mantle the rock platform of the 30-m terrace. Nearly all the exposures are in road cuts, particularly along U. S. Highway 101, and these give a good idea of general distribution along the coast but are not so satisfactory with respect to local relations. Twenty-eight exposures that are certainly eolian in origin have been studied on the stretch of coast between Cape Blanco and Cascade Head (Pl. 1).[46] South of Cape Blanco exposures occur infrequently all the way to the California line. North of Cascade Head on the Oregon and Washington coasts none have been noted, but it is probable that bodies of the ancient dune sand are present, at least as far as Tillamook Head.

Although exact altitudes of road-cut exposures are meaningless, major differences have a certain significance. For the most part the exposures lie within the range of altitude of the 30-m terrace; the deposits within this range would seem to be an integral part of the Elk River beds as defined by Baldwin (1945). In two areas of Region III, beyond the limits of the dune sheet (Localities 20 and 22), ancient eolian sands are found as high as 60 and 90 m (and at lower altitudes as well). These are areas in which there is evidence for a somewhat higher, older terrace level. It is significant also that all but six exposures are adjacent to important bodies of modern dunes—an indication that in the earlier cycle dune development followed a course similar to that of the present one.

Most of the accessible exposures lie at the actual surface of the terrace mantle; only a few are overlain by other types of sediments. This is due to the fact that the dunes represented were formed at the peak of submergence. The ancient eolian masses have lost all trace of dune topography and, where extensive enough, are marked by stream-cut ravines. A typical ancient mass is composed in the main of unconsolidated laminated sand; the laminations dip in various directions and at various angles. One or more much altered podzolic soils are present. The B horizon in these is decidedly indurated, and the materials that have accumulated there have in part moved downward into the underlying unaltered dune sand, forming platelike or conchoidal masses. Roots in their decay have provided easy paths for this transfer, and the firmly cemented casts which have developed around these channels stand out after the loose sand has blown away. Though unconsolidated in the main,

---

[46] The author's own observations have been supplemented by a survey made for him in June, 1951, by Mr. Len Ramp.

the mass is bound into a coherent whole by the indurated podzolic soils and their secondary extensions.

Good exposures of ancient eolian material are seen in highway cuts in Locality 19 from Sutton Lake north for 3 km. Several anastomosing altered podzolic soils are present, and at one point ancient dune sand rests against a steep slope of bedrock. In two localities (20 and 22) ancient eolian sand outcrops in the midst of the active dunes. In Locality 20 (Pl. 22, fig. 2) six much-altered podzolic soils stand out in a steplike series.

The history of these ancient eolian sediments may be reconstructed as follows. During the grand period of submergence preceding the most recent one the sea advanced upon the land, cut a rock platform, and laid upon it a mantle of sediments. Ahead of the sea an interrupted belt of dunes moved inland, and its segments in a general way corresponded in position to the dune masses of today. Repeated local stabilization followed by rejuvenation gave rise to a succession of buried podzolic soils. In certain places the sea rose against dune masses so constituted. Their upper portions were cut away, some of the material was distributed subaqueously by currents, and the rest moved inland before the wind in continuance of dune advance. The basal portions, retaining their dune structure and soil layers, were submerged and most of them buried by subaqueous sedimentation. With rise of sea level, no more eolian material could be added to the sedimentary layer at any given point. The engulfing of eolian sediments must always take place close behind the advancing front of the sea, and only those masses engulfed during the very last part of the submergence period are left accessible for observation. At the end of the period of submergence dune masses still existed at certain points and have remained to the present untouched by the sea. Their extent and magnitude were far less than those of the present day, for the sea had gone much further in reducing their mass and in elimination of receptive shore. The current situation at Tillamook Bay (Locality 7) with its small remnant of a once great dune mass, shows how such reduction can occur.

During the grand period of emergence that followed, fluvial, atmospheric, and biotic factors modified the surface of the slowly broadening coastal plain. Dissection by streams and other agents eliminated all traces of topography due to wind, and physical-chemical changes everywhere modified the structure of the ancient eolian masses.

During the most recent grand period of submergence most of the old coastal-plain surface was destroyed. In places where a narrow strip has survived as a terrace, the ancient eolian masses also persist. Ancient eolian bodies have been overwhelmed by new dunes. Locally where deflation has exposed the substratum, the older indurated sand appears in the midst of the new.

The bodies of ancient eolian sands on the higher levels in localities 20 and 22 may represent a still earlier cycle, second from the latest, in which case they are an integral part of the sedimentary mantle associated with a terrace higher than the youngest, and indicate a history identical to the two later cycles. It is possible, however, that they represent dunes of the next-to-latest cycle that traveled inward and upward farther than others elsewhere.

GENERAL HISTORY OF THE DUNES
TWO MAJOR PERIODS

The history of the modern dunes is tied to two major periods of sea-level change in relation to the land: a grand period of rise with submergence of the coastal lands followed by one in which there is evidence of a small drop with emergence, but which, in comparison with the earlier period, may be considered as characterized by essential stability.

CONDITIONS AT THE BEGINNING OF SUBMERGENCE

The sea level at the beginning of the period of submergence and the distance of the shore line of that time from the present line may be estimated in a rough way. Engineers of the Oregon State Highway Commission, in planning for bridges across the major rivers along the coastal highway, made test borings in the alluvium. The greatest depth reached was 30 m below sea level at Yaquina Bay bridge, very near the inner margin of the 30-m terrace. No rock was encountered at this depth, and the boring was naturally not in mid-channel. Diller (1902), without citing specific evidence, speaks of subsidence to a depth of at least 60 m below present sea level. Somewhat more than 60 m seems to be the minimum possible estimate.[47] With regard to width of the coastal plain at its maximum extension, projection of roughly determined gradients on the present terrace surfaces meets the hypothetical sea level of that time at least 3 km from the inner terrace margin.

The coastal plain[48] that lay below the mountain front had been trenched during the preceding period of emergence by streams flowing across it from the mountains; in certain areas of weak rock wide valleys had been cut. Otherwise dissection had not gone far.

The coastal plain had upon it a certain amount of eolian sediment accumulated during the preceding grand period of emergence. Parallel beach-ridge dunes, quickly stabilized and preserved intact, because of the wet climate and aggressive vegetation of the region, were probably a characteristic feature (cf. the prograded shores of today on both sides of the Columbia River).[49] Throughout the period of low sea level the dune belt was fairly continuous, since the shore line lay beyond the rocky masses that later, as headlands, broke it into segments.

---

[47] There is, of course, the possibility that the last major drop of sea level did not reach a point as low as some previous one, and that a portion of the older alluvial fill was thus left undisturbed.

[48] The distinction here made between coastal plain and terrace is as follows: a coastal plain is conceived as sloping evenly and gently to sea level, whereas a terrace is faced more or less completely with a cliff or bluff leading down to a lower level or to the sea.

[49] It has been implied for several regions that active dunes are readily formed of sand blown from surfaces newly exposed by relative lowering of sea level; e.g., Les Landes of Gascony (Daly, 1934, p. 198), Bermuda, during the glacial ages of the Pleistocene (Sayles, 1931), New Zealand (Brothers, 1954). Although this is not true of the Oregon-Washington coast, it may hold where the stabilizing influences of precipitation and vegetation are not particularly effective. Possibly, in some cases where aggressive dunes have been credited to a "period of emergence", they are to be traced instead to the gradual rise of sea level that brought the period of emergence to an end, during which the advancing sea maintained a constant state of instability at the shore—as on the Oregon-Washington coast.

Shore line in general.—The sea in its advance cut away the unconsolidated sediments that mantled the coastal plain, and parts of the rock beneath. Sea cliffs came into being, and coastal plain was converted step by step into terrace. In due time the advancing sea encountered steep, rocky masses, mainly of volcanic rock, which represented headlands existing at the maximum of the previous submergence. At these points continuity of the terrace was broken. The sea continued its attack upon the intervening areas of weaker rock and constantly reduced the disjointed terrace segments.

Drowning of the river valleys that crossed the coastal plain began with the onset of general submergence. Estuaries came into being; spits and bay bars formed across their mouths. As sea level rose, ponded waters crept steadily up the main valleys, invaded their tributaries, and produced fresh-water lakes with arms.

In certain re-entrants in the mountain front not related to river valleys, sand carried by longshore currents mantled the surface (Region III as a unit is the outstanding example) or a bar developed with a lagoon behind it (Localities 8 and 9). As the sea continued to rise, the mass, even the lagoon, moved inland and upward. The terrace surface, protected from direct attack by waves, passed gently below sea level, and no cliff was formed. Differential earth movements locally complicated this process.

Dunes.—It has been shown that south of Tillamook Head the dunes have moved inland, constantly invading new ground, and that they had already attained stabilization along essentially their line of farthest advance *before* the end of the period of submergence; that north of Tillamook Head, on the contrary, the existing dunes have been built outward from the line of the sea's farthest advance, and therefore *after* the end of the period of submergence. It is necessary, accordingly, to treat the two sectors separately.

SOUTH OF TILLAMOOK HEAD: During the grand period of submergence the dune belt, which may be assumed to have been fairly continuous at the very beginning, became broken into segments separated by stretches of cliff-bounded terrace and high rock masses. The segments dwindled with the extent of receptive shore, and some were eliminated entirely. Older dunes were cut into by the advancing sea, and large quantities of sand passed into deep water and out of circulation. Since, however, rise of sea level does not imply increase in strength of wave attack, but merely its application to new surfaces, there is no reason to assume consequent decrease in amount of sand immediately available to the longshore currents and waves. New sand and old mingled in a state of full mobility. A belt of dunes moved inland; its forms were repeatedly destroyed and reconstituted. Doubtless there were times when the trend of sea-level change was temporarily reversed, allowing rather widespread temporary stabilization.

In time came general stabilization of the dune surfaces—certainly not the first such event, but definitely the culminating one. Advance ended along essentially the present inner margins of the dune masses. This, of course, did not necessarily occur simultaneously in all localities, but the apparently similar age and character of the stabilized masses and their similar relations to subsequent events indicate that their stabilization is to be traced to a set of factors operating simultaneously all along the coast, and that it must therefore be considered a single major event.

The culminating stabilization occurred before the sea had attained its maximum advance. Evidence comes from fourteen localities, extending from the northernmost Locality 5 to Locality 28, just south of Cape Blanco. Stable dune masses, principally parabolas and parabola complexes, have been cut away by the sea in varying degree. On those portions isolated by cliffs no further activity of consequence has been possible. Particularly noteworthy are the truncated complexes north and south of the Umpqua River in Localities 21 and 22 and the surviving parabola tips at Tillamook Bay and Netarts Bay (Localities 7 and 8). Most impressive of all is the remnant upon Cape Kiwanda in Locality 10. Where contact with receptive shore remained, fresh advances have ensued.

Thorough stabilization with a continuously advancing sea behind does not seem reasonable, for an advancing sea is ordinarily a powerful stimulant to dune activity. It seems necessary, therefore, to postulate an interruption of advance—due to a halt in rise of sea level or a period of lowering—long enough to permit development of a deflation plain adjoining the shore and growth of forest upon it, extension of stabilization to the active ridges following automatically. The event was not a simple one, for in several localities recessional ridges developed and were stabilized in turn.

NORTH OF TILLAMOOK HEAD: Whereas south of the Head the great dune masses that were driven inland before the advancing sea and that still survive tell their story quite adequately, direct evidence for events north of the Head during this period is almost totally lacking. Hypothetic reconstruction has been attempted in discussion of Region I, and further comment is unnecessary.

PERIOD SINCE THE MAXIMUM OF SUBMERGENCE

Shore line in general.—The evidence for slight net emergence during this period has been given in detail in the final sections under Regions I, II, and III; the points made may be summarized as follows:

Along the open sea are cliffs separated from the present shore by barrier beaches with lakes and bogs behind them (Region II), and forested wave-cut bluffs fronting terraces and dune masses with wide beaches below (Regions II, III).

On the bay shores of bars and peninsulas are gently sloping aprons merging with tidal flats (Regions I, II), and dune ridges with bases buried by tidal sediments, some with ends previously cut off by tidal currents (Region II).

Dunes south of Tillamook Head.—Since general stabilization with culmination of dune advance antedated maximum sea advance, and since there is no specific event in dune history on this part of the coast that can be correlated with the latter, it is necessary to consider the culmination of dune advance the starting point, even though it precedes maximum submergence. Evidence from six localities well spaced along the coast from Tillamook Head to Cape Blanco indicates that the culminating dune advance was followed by two others which for the most part fell short of the first but have locally overpassed it. In the following discussion, as in previous sections, the culminating advance is designated Episode I and the later ones II and III. Generalizations based upon the evidence derived from these six localities, nos. 5, 9, 19, 23, 24, 25E, will be presented.

Episode I is represented in all localities by a stabilized precipitation ridge, which in some has "recessional" ridges closely associated with it; by isolated remnant masses in Localities 23 and 25E; and in most localities by an almost completely reduced deflation plain. In Localities 23 and 25E a plain seaward of the ridge remnants must be postulated, since development of vegetation on such a surface is prerequisite to stabilization of mobile masses inland from it. The whole area representing Episode I is stabilized and forested almost completely. For attainment of this condition a lengthy period of freedom from sand movement from the shore must be assumed.

The area related to Episode II is far less homogeneous than the older one and less advanced developmentally. Four localities (5, 9, 19, 24) have stabilized precipitation ridges, with or without recessional ridges; and in one of these (Locality 19) the deflation plain is far from completely reduced. In the other two (Localities 23 and 25E) the precipitation ridges are active though cut off from source of supply; the first still retains the character of a massive, though senescent, oblique-ridge system. The deflation plain in Locality 23 is very incompletely reduced, and there are many spots of current activity. In Locality 25E the deflation plain, still bare next to the precipitation ridge, is undergoing invasion by vegetation from the west. The period during which the deflation plains of Episode II developed was shorter than the earlier one or else quiescence was less perfect.

The areas representing Episode III are everywhere in contact with receptive shore, from which sand moves freely inland to the advancing front, except that in Localities 19, 24, and 25E incipient vegetation makes a rudimentary barrier. In general, present activity in a given locality follows the pattern already set. In Localities 5, 24, and 25E, for example, there is an active precipitation ridge. Locality 9 shows an active strip along the axis of the parabola. In Locality 23 development of the oblique-ridge system is being repeated on a smaller scale. Episode III in Locality 19 is still in an early stage, and development has been highly irregular. An orderly pattern matching previous episodes should in time emerge.

A second group of eight localities (10, 14, 16, 20, 21, 22, 26A, 30) differs from the six just considered in showing only an undifferentiated strip of stabilized dunes with outliers, and an outer active zone. The inner strips in this group with their outliers are assigned to Episode I. Episode II and III seem to have merged as far as visible results are concerned. In a third group (7, 8, 15, 18, 28), where only a fragment of the old stabilized mass remains, entirely cut off from fresh supply, evidence as to Episodes II and III is completely lacking.

Dunes north of Tillamook Head.—The key factor for the history here is the Columbia River. Though not classed as an important sediment-bearing stream as far as material in suspension is concerned, it carries a formidable bed load of sand that in summer freshets travels down the river in waves which near the mouth of the Willamette River range from 2.5 m to more than 4 m in height (U. S. Army Corps of Engineers, Portland District, personal communication). The shoals at the river mouth, which made entry and egress hazardous until the jetties were built, are the product of this mass movement, and the pronounced bulge of the 10-fathom line (U. S. Coast and Geodetic Survey, Charts 6002, 6151) is additional evidence of it. Longshore currents carry the sand from the river both north and south. The greater part apparently goes northward, and this is augmented by bed-load material moving out from Willapa Bay and Grays Harbor; the 10-fathom line bulges opposite their mouths as it does at the Columbia, but on a lesser scale.

When comparative stability or slight fall of sea level superseded submergence, progradation was no longer inhibited and abundant materials were available to the longshore currents from the Columbia, made even more abundant, probably, by shallowing of the river which brought its ample bed load nearer the surface. Active progradation north of Tillamook Head opposed to almost none south of it, directly inhibiting factors being absent in both, seems clearly traceable to difference in sand supply: on the north a tremendous load carried by a mighty river, supplemented by contributions from adjacent streams draining sand-rich terrain; on the south the small amounts provided by rivers mostly with limited, completely forested watersheds and settling basins at their mouths, spaced at wide intervals on a lengthy coast. No bulges opposite the mouths of these rivers appear on the coast charts.

The first beach ridge was formed at the base of the wave-cut bluffs or close to it and along the outer margin of the bars. One by one new ridges were added, and the forelands and peninsulas became constantly wider. The process was not without interruptions. North of the Columbia, where progradation was more vigorous, there was apparently only one brief reversal. Between the Columbia and Tillamook Head interruptions have been more frequent. It is possible that here, where sand supply has been less abundant, conditions at the shore have been more susceptible to the effects of small disturbing factors.

TENTATIVE CORRELATION OF DUNE HISTORY WITH GLACIER AND CLIMATIC CHANGES

Correlation with events of late Pleistocene time.—It is quite evident that the grand period of submergence, so important in the history of the dunes, is the obverse of the eustatic rise of sea level that accompanied decline and disappearance of the continental ice sheets of North America and Europe. The name Flandrian, applied in Europe to the sediments laid down during this marine transgression (Flint, 1957, p. 262), transferred to the eustatic rise itself, is a useful term in the present situation, since it applies directly to sea-level behavior. The Flandrian rise was succeeded by a period characterized by comparative stability of sea level (McFarlan, 1955; Brannan *et al.*, 1957); this corresponds with the second great period in dune history.

The turning point in coastal history affecting dune development is thus the end of the Flandrian rise. It must be placed at some point during the relatively warm "mid-post-Pleistocene" period for which the most recently proposed name is Hypsithermal (Deevey and Flint, 1957). The considerable lag behind the causative climatic change is indicated by data given by Flint (1957, p. 262) that imply a sea level at least 36 m lower than now in early Hypsithermal (Boreal) time and 17 m lower at the beginning of Atlantic time.

Deevey and Flint (1957, Table 1) date their Hypsithermal in C^{14} years from about 9500 B.P. to about 2600 B.P. If the end of Flandrian time is placed approximately in the middle of the Hypsithermal, at 6000 B.P., the period of dune advance in Regions II–IV had a length of about 12,000 years—from the assumed maximum of Wisconsin glaciation at 18,000 B.P. (Flint, 1957, p. 325 and Fig. 18-8) to 6000 B.P. By far the greatest part of the changes in coastal features—rise in sea level (minimum total 60 m), advance of sea upon the land (several km), cutting back of coastal cliffs, invasion by dunes—must have been wrought since the maximum of Valders-Mankato glaciation, when the sharply increased rate of glacier melting began that finally resulted in disappearance of the subarctic ice sheets (Ericson *et al.*, 1956, p. 387). This maximum has been radiocarbon-dated at about 11,000 B.P.; 5000 years seems a short time indeed into which to crowd so many events of so great magnitude. The 6000 years of post-Flandrian time, on the other hand, seem adequate for accomplishment of the progradational developments in Region I. Support for the latter estimate is found in a report by McFarlan (1955) in which C^{14} analyses of wood and shell from beneath the Mississippi deltaic plain and adjacent portions of the continental shelf indicate that ". . . . the late phase of the cycle, the epoch of standing sea level, began approximately 5000 years ago. . . ."

Direct influence of climatic changes.—Although eustatic sea-level change has been the major controlling force in the course of known dune history, climatic factors acting directly have had their share of influence. In the region covered by this study the half-cycle progression of climatic elements relevant to dune phenomena, from glacial to interglacial, is theoretically as follows:

GLACIAL: Storm tracks at their southern limit; maximum storminess and precipitation; dry season very short or absent; southwesterly winter gales at maximum frequency, and steady north-northwesterly winds of summer at minimum. Changing gradually to—

INTERGLACIAL: Storm tracks at northern limit; minimum storminess and precipitation; summer dry season long; southwesterly winter gales at minimum and north-northwesterly winds of summer at maximum.

The general climatic progression during the period covered by this study of the modern dunes has been from glacial conditions at the Wisconsin maximum to a stage somewhat closer to interglacial at the present, then a small backward shift toward the glacial. In the earlier part of the deglaciation period conditions were favorable for initiation and amplification, in suitable places, of massive parabola complexes with axes oriented with the southwesterly winter gales; 10 out of 12 such structures are so oriented. These winds were not, however, so exclusively in control as to inhibit general inland advance where receptive shore was extensive as in Region III and most of Region IV. The transverse-ridge pattern, purely a product of the summer wind, had little chance for development in earlier times but increased in importance as the dry season lengthened and the winds of that season became more potent. The small shift toward glacial climatic conditions that came with the end of the Hypsithermal—to be carefully distinguished from the accompanying change in sea level—seems not to have had an appreciable effect on the course of dune history.

Influence of vegetation history.—Since vegetation type affects dune morphology so profoundly, it is important to know whether the climatic progression has modified this factor. Hansen has constructed a number of pollen profiles derived from bogs in and near the dunes. One of these bogs is significant in that it lies at the east margin of Woahink Lake (Locality 20), one of the large water bodies that owe their existence to the dunes. Hansen (1941; 1947) considers that peat deposition here required most or all of "post-glacial" time. His pollen diagram (1947, p. 96) shows that Sitka spruce was predominant throughout the history with western hemlock, Douglas fir, and lodgepole pine in descending order of importance. No large-scale changes in relative frequency occurred. Diagrams from other coastal bogs confirm this pattern. In Hansen's words (1947, p. 95): "The postglacial climate of the north Pacific coast has probably been essentially marine, with little variation, even during the dry period that developed farther inland. While climatic fluctuations undoubtedly did occur, they were of insufficient magnitude to cause a systematic response by the vegetation." The dry period referred to is the Hypsithermal. Phytogenic dune development in the "postglacial" past must therefore have been essentially the same as it is today. A similar assertion may be made with regard to preceding periods. Beds of plant remains, both macroscopic and microscopic, which have not as yet been precisely dated, show that the vegetation factor in the system, well back into the Pleistocene, has been essentially a constant (Hansen and Allison, 1942; Baldwin, 1945; Snavely, 1948).

Hierarchy of cyclic events.—The dune history comprises recurring periods of change with repetition of similar events that in a broad sense may be regarded as cyclic. The cycle of first magnitude is related to periods of glaciation: from the maximum of one glacial age through the following interglacial to the maximum of the next glacial. The known history of the modern dunes covers a part of one of these. The principal events of this segment of a cycle have been recorded, and the immediate causes thereof have been discussed; the most important are eustatic sea-level changes and climatic changes associated with the glacial story.

Upon this major cycle are superposed others of a second rank. Episode I, representing the culmination of advance, was a surge of activity that originated at the shore and moved inland. Episodes II and III may be assumed to have been similar surges with similar causes, but on a lesser scale.

The considerable length of coast exhibiting a uniform sequence of dune advances suggests the possibility that the stimulant to advance in these cases—the "trigger action" that started them on their way—has been a small eustatic sea-level rise associated with a minor episode of glacier shrinkage. If so, similar dune sequences should be found on widely distributed coasts favorable to their development. There is a certain amount of evidence to this effect.

The coastal dunes of Les Landes in southwestern France (Durègne, 1902; Duffart, 1904; Harlé and Harlé, 1920; Buffault, 1942) show well-marked stages. The oldest sheet, the "continental dunes", may be ignored, since there seems to be general agreement that its materials are not from the sea. The "maritime dunes" are divided into "ancient" or "primary", and "modern" dunes. The pattern of the ancient dunes is one of closely imbricated parabolas aligned with westerly winds; they are completely stabilized and forested. Buffault concluded from evidence derived from borings that the primary dunes include two sand sheets, each of which acquired a thick layer of "alios" (compact B horizon of a podzolic soil) with forest, indicating periods of stabilization of considerable length. The modern dunes consist of several very massive and extended wavelike ridges parallel to the shore, with long narrow depressions, or "lettes" between. The two sheets of primary dunes and the modern dunes are the suggested counterparts of the three surges of the Oregon-Washington coast. The modern wave dunes with a wide flat strip outside them suggest a series of precipitation ridges and a deflation plain. Buffault even suggests a process of development for a "wave dune" almost identical with that proposed for the "precipitation ridge" in the present study, though naturally not in the same terms: its origin at the seaward edge of the forest, which it overtops and destroys as it advances inland. There is confirmatory evidence for this process in numerous exposures at the shore line of alios with stumps in place, uncovered by the receding dunes and eroded by the waves. Before artificial stabilization (initiated by Brémontier in 1787) the modern dunes were actively invading the primary dunes and had overpassed them in many places. Buffault thought that the modern dunes did not begin to form before the 5th century A. D. Harlé and Harlé estimated that building of the maritime dunes has required about 6000 years; their computation is based on

$$\frac{\text{total volume per unit frontage}}{\text{present annual increment}}.$$

A second apparent parallel to the Oregon sequence is reported from New Zealand by Brothers (1954). On the west coast of the North Island, northwest of Auckland, are three dune belts. The dunes of the oldest originated at the base of a bluff 150 m high cut by the sea in poorly consolidated Pleistocene sandstone at the culmination of Flandrian sea-level rise. They have ascended the gullied bluff to its top, and have given rise there to long tapering ridges aligned with the dominant winds. They support a fairly dense vegetation cover, but there has been much rejuvenation. The second belt, only 400 m wide, is made up of three or four massive ridges, roughly parallel with the shore, with elongate depressions between, and overlapping the dunes of the first belt at 6–15 m above sea level. The vegetation is a scant cover of grasses. The third belt, about 3 km wide, is actively invading the second, and at one point has overpassed the first. A marram-grass foredune is at present undergoing erosion. This entire sequence has come to pass since culmination of the Flandrian rise, which, according to Brothers, attained a height of 2.4–3.7 m above present sea level. It has involved considerable progradation, which, however, has manifested itself in a way quite different from the building of beach ridges adjacent to the Columbia River. Brothers offers as an explanation of the sequence an alternation of periods of calm climatic conditions favoring progradation and dune building with periods of generally stormy weather causing retrogradation and dune destruction—a hypothesis that may be true for his region either in opposition to the hypothesis of eustatic sea-level change or supplementary to it.

Another sequence appears at Port Kembla, New South Wales (McElroy, 1953). A vertical section 500 m behind the present shore line reveals three cycles of dune activity. The oldest sheet has a very thick iron-pan B horizon; its surface supported trees up to 1 m in diameter. The next younger sheet has a thinner B horizon; the uppermost layer was deposited in relatively recent time.

These cases are offered not as being in any degree conclusive but rather as an incentive to further use of sand-dune phenomena in interpretation of general coastal history. There are, of course, other conceivable hypotheses to explain the surges of activity alternating with periods of quiescence on the Oregon coast if world-wide correlation of sequences cannot be established. Any such hypothesis must explain initiation and cessation of activity at the shore, periodic changes in amount of sand supply from the shore with almost complete failure for long periods, and essentially synchronous sequence of events over a coast line 500 km long. Climatic fluctuations seem to offer the only possibilities. They might include periodic changes in degree of storminess (*cf.* Brothers), in wind velocity, in wind direction, acting singly or in combination.

Surges of activity of a still lower order of magnitude have been noted as occurring in Localities 9, 19, and 22, all of them minor events superposed upon Episode III. In each case there is a series of three or four advancing waves; in Locality 19 the oldest have forested deflation surfaces behind them that are being invaded by the next in order. Alternation of abundant sand supply with almost none is the obvious direct cause; the more fundamental factors may be one or more of those listed in the preceding paragraph.

The latest event in world climatic history is the comparatively warm period of the last 1–2 centuries, which has resulted in moderate glacier contraction. Rise of sea level is to be expected as a further consequence, and tide-gauge records show that it is actually in progress. The rate for the last hundred years is estimated by Flint (1957, p. 261) to be a little more than 1 mm per year. Marmer (1949) gives data from tide-gauge measurements on the Atlantic and Pacific coasts of the United States. The average for 5 stations on the Atlantic coast (Massachusetts to Florida) for the period 1930–1947 is .61 cm per year. Three stations on the Pacific coast (San Pedro, San Francisco, Seattle) show a rise for the period 1930–1947; the rate is only a third of that for the Atlantic coast. In all probability tied to the current advance of the sea is the fact that on most dune frontages there is a present state of marked activity at the shore. It is manifest in inland travel of sand by progression of transverse ridges, eroding of certain stabilized dune masses, and partial stripping of forest from eroded slopes of old dunes stabilized since the end of the grand period of submergence. The current surge is, however, at least up to the present, simply the latest phase of Episode III; its effects are as yet only dimly distinguishable from those of the episode as a whole.

Earlier dune cycle in relation to glacier history.—All accessible exposures (except a few somewhat higher up) lie close to the inner edge of the mantle of unconsolidated materials associated with the 30-m terrace. They therefore date from the culmination of the grand period of submergence preceding the latest grand period of emergence—the latter coinciding with the Wisconsin glacial age. Carrying backward the line of reasoning with respect to the modern dunes, it may be assumed that during the rise of sea level associated with Illinoian deglaciation a dune belt, at first fairly continuous, moved inland, became broken into segments, and finally, at the extreme limit of sea advance, almost disappeared due to destruction of stabilized masses and practical elimination of receptive shore. In the present cycle this extremity has not been reached. Should there be continued extensive deglaciation it would inevitably be attained. A similar course of events is postulated for the earlier glacial ages and interglacials of the Pleistocene.

In concluding this history it must be emphasized once again that the sequence of events presented is the minimum required to account for the known facts. Influences and events that lie hidden would, if revealed, make the history more complex and would doubtless necessitate modification of some of the interpretations presented.

REFERENCES CITED

Ackerman, E. A. (1941) *The Köppen classification of climates in North America*, Geog. Rev., vol. 31, p. 105–111

Allen, J. E., and Baldwin, E. M. (1944) *Geology and coal resources of the Coos Bay quadrangle, Oregon*, Oreg. Dept. Geol. and Mineral Industries, Bull. 27, 157 p.

Arnold, Ralph (1906) *Geological reconnaissance of the coast of the Olympic Peninsula, Washington*, Geol. Soc. Am., Bull., vol. 17, p. 451–468

Arnst, Albert (1942a) *Vegetal stabilization of Oregon coastal dunes*, Northwest Science, vol. 16, p. 59–67

———— (1942b) *Trees against the wind*, Am. Forests, vol. 48, p. 543–545, 562, 576

Aufrère, L. (1931) *Le cycle morphologique des dunes*, Ann. de Géog., vol. 40, p. 362–385

———— (1933) *Les dunes continentales, leurs rapports avec le sous-sol, le passé géologique récent et le climat actuel*, Comptes Rendus du Congrès Intern. de Géog., Paris, 1931, Tome 2, p. 699–711

———— (1935) *Essai sur les dunes du Sahara Algérien*, Geografiska Annaler, vol. 17, Special Supplement: Hyllingsskrift tillägnad Sven Hedin, på hans 70 Årsdag, den 19 Febr., 1935, p. 481–498

Bagnold, R. A. (1935) *The movement of desert sand*, Geog. Jour., vol. 85, p. 342–369

———— (1937) *The transport of sand by wind*, Geog. Jour., vol. 89, p. 409–438

———— (1941) *The physics of blown sand and desert dunes*, William Morrow and Co., N. Y., 265 p.

Baldwin, E. M. (1945) *Some revisions of the late Cenozoic stratigraphy of the southern Oregon coast*, Jour. Geol., vol. 45, p. 35–46

Bancroft, H. H. (1888) *History of Oregon*, vol. 2. The History Co., San Francisco, 808 p.

Baschin, Otto (1899) *Die Entstehung wellenähnlicher Oberflächenformen*, Zeitschr. der Ges. für Erdkunde zu Berlin, Ser. III, vol. 34, p. 408–424

———— (1903) *Dünenstudien*, Zeitschr. der Ges. für Erdkunde zu Berlin, 1903, p. 422–430

Beadnell, H. J. L. (1910) *The sand-dunes of the Libyan Desert. Their origin, form, and rate of movement, considered in relation to the geological and meteorological conditions of the region*, Geog. Jour., vol. 35, p. 379–395

Bertololy, E. (1900) *Kräuselungsmarken und Dünen*, Münchener Geog. Studien, 9

Binder, R. C. (1949) *Fluid mechanics*, Prentice-Hall Inc., N. Y., 361 p.

Bourcart, Jacques (1938) *L'action du vent à la surface de la terre*, Rev. de Géog. Physique et de Géol. Dynamique, vol. 1, p. 194–265

Bowman, Isaiah (1916) *The Andes of Southern Peru*, Pub. for Am. Geog. Soc. by Henry Holt and Co., N. Y., 336 p.

———— (1924) *Desert trails of Atacama*, Am. Geog. Soc., Spec. Pub., No. 5, 362 p.

Brannan, H. R., Jr., Simons, L. H., Perry, D., Daughtry, A. C., and McFarlan, E., Jr. (1957) *Humble Oil Co. radiocarbon dates II*, Science, 125, p. 919–923

Braun, Gustav (1911) *Entwicklungsgeschichtliche Studien an europäischen Flachlandsküsten und ihren Dünen*, Veröff. des Inst. für Meereskunde und des geog. Inst. an der Univ. Berlin, Heft 15, p. 1–174

Briquet, A. (1923) *Les dunes littorales*, Ann. de Géog., vol. 32, p. 385–394

Brothers, R. N. (1954) *A physiographic study of recent sand dunes on the Auckland west coast*, New Zealand Geographer, vol. 10, p. 47–59

Brunt, David (1939) *Physical and dynamical meteorology*, Cambridge Univ. Press, Cambridge, England, 411 p.

Bucher, W. H. (1919) *The origin of ripples and related sedimentary surface forms*, Am. Jour. Sci., 4th Ser., vol. 47, p. 149–210, 243–269

Buffault, Pierre (1942) *Histoire des dunes maritimes de la Gascogne*, Éditions Delmas, Bordeaux, 446 p.

Capot-Rey, R. (1945) *Dry and humid morphology in the Western Erg*, Geog. Rev., vol. 35, p. 391–407

Capot-Rey, R., and Capot-Rey, F. (1948) *Le déplacement des sables éoliens et la formation des dunes désertiques, d'après R. A. Bagnold*, Trav. de l'Inst. de Recherches Sahariennes, Tome 5, p. 47–80

Chase, A. W. (1873) *Indian mounds and relics on the coast of Oregon*, Am. Jour. Sci., 3d Ser., vol. 6, p. 26–32

Cholnoky, E. (1902) *Die Bewegungsgesetze des Flugsandes*, Földtani Közlöny, Bd. 32, Budapest

Cockayne, L. (1911) *Report on the dune areas of New Zealand, their geology, botany, and reclamation*, John Mackay, Govt. Printer, Wellington, N. Z., 76 p.

Cooper, W. S. (1935) *The history of the upper Mississippi River in late Wisconsin and postglacial time*, Minn. Geol. Surv., Bull. 26, 116 p.

———— (1936) *The strand and dune flora of the Pacific coast of North America*, p. 141–187 *in* Goodspeed, T. H., *Editor*, Essays in geobotany in honor of William Albert Setchell, Univ. Calif. Press, 319 p.

———— (1938) *Ancient dunes of the upper Mississippi valley as possible climatic indicators*, Am. Meteorol. Soc., Bull. 19, p. 193–204

———— (1944) *Development and maintenance of the mature profile of a transverse dune ridge*, Am. Philos. Soc., Year Book, 1944, p. 150–153

———— (1957) *Vegetation of the Northwest American Province*, 8th Pac. Sci. Cong. of the Pac. Sci. Assoc., 1953, Proc., p. 133–138

Cornish, Vaughan (1897) *On the formation of sand dunes*, Geog. Jour., vol. 9, p. 278–309

———— (1900) *On desert sand dunes bordering the Nile delta*, Geog. Jour., vol. 15, p. 1–32

———— (1908) *On the observation of desert sand dunes*, Geog. Jour., vol. 31, p. 400–402

———— (1914) *Waves of sand and snow and the eddies which make them*, T. Fisher Unwin, London, 383 p.

Cotton, C. A. (1949) *Geomorphology*, 5th ed., John Wiley and Sons, Inc., N. Y., 505 p.

Cowles, H. C. (1899) *The ecological relations of the vegetation on the sand dunes of Lake Michigan*, Bot. Gaz., vol. 27, p. 95–117, 167–202, 281–308, 361–391

Cressman, L. S. (1946) *Early man in Oregon: stratigraphic evidence*, Sci. Mo., vol. 62, p. 43–51

Cressy, G. B. (1928) *The Indiana sand dunes and shore lines of the Lake Michigan basin*, Geog. Soc. Chicago, Bull. 6, 80 p.

Dachnowski-Stokes, A. P. (1936) *Peat lands in the Pacific coast states in relation to land and water resources*, U. S. Dept. Agric., Miscel. Pub., No. 248, 68 p.

Daly, R. A. (1934) *The changing world of the ice age*, Yale Univ. Press, New Haven, 271 p.

Dana, J. D. (1849) *in* United States exploring expedition, during the years 1838, 1839, 1840, 1841, 1842, under the command of Charles Wilkes, U. S. N., vol. X, Geology, Philadelphia, C. Sherman, 756 p.

Darwin, G. H. (1884) *On the formation of ripple-mark in sand*, Roy. Soc. London, Proc., vol. 36, p. 18–43

Deevey, E. S., and Flint, R. F. (1957) *Postglacial hypsithermal interval*, Science, vol. 125, p. 182–184

van Dieren, J. W. (1934) *Organogene Dünenbildung. Eine geomorphologische Analyse der Dünenlandschaft der West-Friesischen Insel Terschelling mit pflanzensoziologischen Methoden*, Martinus Nijhoff, Haag, 304 p.

Diller, J. S. (1895–1896) *A geological reconnaissance in northwestern Oregon*, U. S. Geol. Survey, 17th Ann. Rep., Pt. 1, p. 441–520

———— (1901) U. S. Geol. Survey, Geol. Atlas, Coos Bay Folio (No. 73)

———— (1902) *Topographic development of the Klamath Mountains*, U. S. Geol. Survey, Bull. 196, 69 p.

———— (1903) U. S. Geol. Survey, Geol. Atlas, Port Orford Folio (No. 89)

Dobrowolski, L. (1924) *Mouvements de l'air et l'eau sur les accidents du sol*, Geografiska Annaler, vol. 6, p. 300–367

Dodge, R. A., and Thompson, M. J. (1937) *Fluid mechanics*, McGraw-Hill Book Co., N. Y., 495 p.

Dommasch, D. O. (1953) *Principles of aerodynamics*, Pitman Pub. Co., N. Y., Toronto, London, 389 p.

Dryden, H. L. (1941) *The role of transition from laminar to turbulent flow in fluid mechanics*, p. 1–13, *in* Fluid mechanics and statistical methods in engineering, Univ. Penn. Bicentennial Conference, 146 p.

Dryden, H. L., Murnaghan, F. D., and Bateman, H. (1932) Report of the Committee on Hydrodynamics, Division of Physical Sciences, National Research Council, Nat. Res. Council, Bull., No. 84, 634 p.

Duffart, C. (1904) *Les formations éoliennes du Plateau Landais,* Congrès de Sociétés Savantes de Paris, section des Sciences, Comptes Rendus, 1904, p. 115–117

Durègne, E. (1902) *Contribution à l'étude des dunes. Dunes anciennes de Gascogne,* Actes Soc. Linn. Bordeaux, vol. 57, p. 1–15

Dwinnell, J. H. (1949) *Principles of aerodynamics,* McGraw-Hill Book Co., N. Y., 391 p.

Egler, F. E. (1934) *Communities and successional trends in the vegetation of the Coos Bay sand dunes, Oregon,* M. S. thesis, Univ. of Minnesota, 39 p.

von Engeln, O. D. (1942) *Geomorphology: systematic and regional,* The MacMillan Co., N. Y., 655 p.

von Engeln, O. D., and Caster, K. E. (1952) *Geology,* McGraw-Hill Book Co., N. Y., 730 p.

Enquist, Fredrik (1932) *The relation between dune-form and wind-direction,* Geol. Fören. i Stockholm, Förhandl., vol. 54, p. 19–59

Ericson, D. B., Broecker, W. S., Kulp, J. L., and Wollin, G. (1956) *Late-Pleistocene climates and deep-sea sediments,* Science, vol. 124, p. 385–389

Exner, F. M. (1920) *Zur physik der Dünen,* Sitzungsber. Akad. Wiss. Wien, Math. Naturw. Kl., Abt. 2a, Ed. 129, p. 929–952

———— (1921) *Dünen und Mäander, Wellenformen der festen Erdoberflache, deren Wachstum und Bewegung,* Geografiska Annaler, vol. 3, p. 327–335

———— (1927) *Über Dünen und Sandwellen,* Geografiska Annaler, vol. 9, p. 81–89

Fenneman, N. M. (1931) *Physiography of Western United States,* McGraw-Hill Book Co., N. Y., 534 p.

Flint, R. F. (1957) *Glacial and Pleistocene geology,* John Wiley and Sons, Inc., N. Y., 553 p.

Free, E. E. (1911) *The movement of soil material by the wind, with a bibliography of eolian geology by S. C. Stuntz and E. E. Free,* U. S. Dept. Agric., Bur. Soils, Bull. 68, 272 p.

Garrels, R. M. (1951) *A textbook of geology,* Harper and Brothers, N. Y., 511 p.

Geological Society of America (1952) Map of Pleistocene eolian deposits of the United States, Alaska and parts of Canada, Thorp, James, and Smith, H. T. U., *Co-chairmen*

Glover, S. L. (1940) *Pleistocene deformation in the Olympic coastal region,* Northwest Science, vol. 14, p. 69–71

Goldstein, S. (1938) *Editor, Modern developments in fluid dynamics,* 2 vols., Oxford, The Clarendon Press

Griggs, A. B. (1945) *Chromite-bearing sands of the southern part of the coast of Oregon,* U. S. Geol. Survey, Bull., 945-E, p. 113–150

Hack, J. T. (1941) *Dunes of the western Navajo country,* Geog. Rev., vol. 31, p. 240–263

Hahmann, Peter (1912) *Die Bildung von Sanddünen bei gleichmässiger Strömung,* Annaler der Physik, 4th Ser., vol. 39, p. 637–676

Hansen, H. P. (1941) *Paleoecology of two peat deposits on the Oregon coast,* Oreg. State Monographs; Studies in Botany, vol. 3, p. 1–31

———— (1944) *Further pollen studies of peat bogs on the Pacific coast of Oregon and Washington,* Bull. Torrey Bot. Club, vol. 71, p. 627–636

———— (1947) *Postglacial forest succession, climate, and chronology in the Pacific Northwest,* Am. Philos. Soc., Trans., New Ser., vol. 37, pt. 1, p. 1–130

Hansen, H. P., and Allison, I. S. (1942) *A pollen study of a fossil peat deposit on the Oregon coast,* Northwest Science, vol. 16, p. 86–92

Harlé, E., and Harlé, J. (1920) *Mémoire sur les dunes de Gascogne avec observations sur la formation des dunes,* Bull. du Comité des Travaux Historiques et Scientifiques, Sec. de Géographie, vol. 34, p. 1–145

Hartnack, W. (1925) *Wanderdünen Pommerns, ihre Form und Entstehung,* Druck und Verlag von Julius Abel, Greifswald, 112 p.

Haurwitz, B. (1941) *Dynamic meteorology*, McGraw-Hill Book Co., N. Y., 365 p.

Hedin, Sven (1904) *Scientific results of a journey in central Asia, 1899–1902*, vols. 1 and 2, Stockholm

Helmholtz, H. von (1889) *Über atmosphärische Bewegung*, Sitzungsber. der Königl. Preuss. Akad. der Wissenschaften zu Berlin, 1889, p. 761–780

Henry, A. J. (1926) *Simpson on the velocity equivalents of the Beaufort scale*, Mo. Weather Rev., vol. 54, p. 298

Högbom, Ivar (1923) *Ancient inland dunes of northern and middle Europe*, Geografiska Annaler, vol. 5, p. 113–242

House, H. D. (1914a) *The sand dunes of Coos Bay, Oregon*, Plant World, vol. 17, p. 238–243

——— (1914b) *Vegetation of the Coos Bay region, Oregon*, Muhlenbergia, vol. 9, p. 81–100

——— (1918) *Forests of the Coos Bay region, Oregon*, The Biltmorean, vol. 5, p. 3–8

Hume, W. F. (1921) *The Egyptian wilderness*, Geog. Jour., vol. 58, p. 249–276

Jentsch, K. A. (1900) *Die Geologie der Dünen*, *in* Gerhardt, Handbuch des deutschen Dünenbaues, Pt. I, p. 1–124

Johnson, G. R. (1930) *Peru from the air*, Am. Geog. Soc., Spec. Pub., No. 12, 158 p.

Jones, Bradley (1942) *Elements of practical aerodynamics*, 3d ed., John Wiley and Sons, Inc., N. Y., 459 p.

von Kármán, Theodore (1954) *Aerodynamics: selected topics in the light of their historical development*, Cornell Univ. Press, Ithaca, N. Y., 203 p.

Kellogg, F. B. (1915) *Sand-dune reclamation on the coast of northern California and southern Oregon*, Soc. Am. Foresters, Proc., vol. 10, p. 41–64

King, W. J. Harding (1918) *Study of a dune belt*, Geog. Jour., vol. 51, p. 16–33. Discussion, Geog. Jour., vol. 51, p. 250–258

Kirkaldy, J. E. (1954) *General principles of geology*, Hutchinson's Scientific and Technical Publications, London and N. Y., 327 p.

Kuethe, A. M., and Schetzer, J. D. (1950) *Foundations of aerodynamics*, John Wiley and Sons, Inc., N. Y., 374 p.

Lahee, F. H. (1923) *Field geology*, McGraw-Hill Book Co., N. Y., 528 p.

Lamb, F. H. (1898) *Sand-dune reclamation on the Pacific coast*, The Forester, vol. 4, p. 141–142

Landsberg, H. (1942) *The structure of the wind over a sand dune*, Am. Geophys. Union, Trans., vol. 23, p. 237–239

Landsberg, H., and Riley, N. A. (1943) *Wind influences on the transportation of sand over a Michigan sand dune*, Second Hydraulics Conference, Proc., Univ. Iowa, Studies in Engineering, Bull. 27, p. 342–352

Langmuir, Irving (1938) *Surface motion of water induced by wind*, Science, vol. 87, p. 119–123

Lawrence, D. B. (1939) *Some features of the Columbia River gorge with special reference to asymmetry in forest trees*, Ecol. Mono., vol. 9, p. 217–257

Leet, L. D., and Judson, Sheldon (1954) *Physical geology*, Prentice-Hall, Inc., N. Y., 466 p.

Lewis, Meriwether, and Clark, William, ed. by R. G. Thwaites (1905) *Original journals of the Lewis and Clark expedition, 1804–1806*, vol. 3, Dodd, Mead and Co., N. Y., 363 p.

Liepmann, H. W. and Puckett, A. E. (1947) *Introduction to aerodynamics of a compressible fluid*, John Wiley and Sons, Inc., N. Y., 262 p.

Lobeck, A. K. (1939) *Geomorphology*, McGraw-Hill Book Co., N. Y., 731 p.

Lomas, J. (1907) *Desert conditions and the origin of the British Trias*, Liverpool Geol. Soc., Proc., vol. 10, 1906–1907, p. 172–197

Lowry, W. D., and Baldwin, E. M. (1952) *Late Cenozoic geology of the lower Columbia River valley, Oregon and Washington*, Geol. Soc. Am., Bull., vol. 63, p. 1–24

Lupton, C. T. (1915) *Oil and gas in the western part of the Olympic Peninsula, Washington*, U. S. Geol. Survey, Bull. 581, p. 23–81

McElroy, C. T. (1953) *Successive profile development in sand dunes at Port Kembla, New South Wales*, Austr. Jour. Sci., vol. 16, p. 112–115

McFarlan, E., Jr. (1955) *Radiocarbon dating of the late Quaternary in southern Louisiana* (abstract), Geol. Soc. Am. Bull., vol. 66, p. 1594–1595

McLaughlin, W. T. (1939) *Planting for topographic control on the Warrenton, Oregon coastal dune area*, Northwest Science, vol. 13, p. 26–32

McLaughlin, W. T., and Brown, R. L. (1942) *Controlling sand dunes in the Pacific Northwest*, U. S. Dept. Agric., Circ. No. 660, 46 p.

Madigan, C. T. (1936) *The Australian sand-ridge deserts*, Geog. Rev., vol. 26, p. 205–227

————— (1946) *The sand formations, in* The Simpson desert expedition, 1939. Scientific Reports: No. 6, Geology, Roy. Soc. South Austr., Trans., vol. 70, p. 45–63

Marmer, H. A. (1949) *Sea level changes along the coasts of the United States in recent years*, Am. Geophys. Union, Trans., vol. 30, p. 201–204

Maxson, J. H. (1932) *Geomorphic features of northwesternmost California* (Abstract), Geol. Soc. Am. Bull., vol. 43, p. 224

Medlicott, H. B., and Blanford, W. T. (1893) *A manual of the geology of India*, 2nd ed., revised by R. D. Oldham, India Geological Survey, Calcutta, 543 p.

Melton, F. A. (1940) *A tentative classification of sand dunes; its application to dune history in the southern high plains*, Jour. Geol., vol. 48, p. 113–145

Milne-Thomson, L. M. (1948) *Theoretical aerodynamics*, MacMillan and Co., London, 363 p.

Olsson-Seffer, Pehr (1908) *Relation of wind to topography of coastal drift sands*, Jour. Geol., vol. 16, p. 549–564

————— (1910) *Genesis and development of sand formations on marine coasts*, Augustana Library, Pub. No. 7, p. 10–41

Pardee, J. T. (1934) *Beach placers of the Oregon coast*, U. S. Geol. Survey Circ. 8, p. 1–41

Peterson, Emil, and Powers, Alfred (1952) *A century of Coos and Curry*, Binfords and Mort, Portland, Oregon, 599 p.

Piercy, N. A. V. (1937) *Aerodynamics*. The English Universities Press, London, 423 p.

Prandtl, L. (1927) *The generation of vortices in fluids of small viscosity*, Royal Aeronaut. Soc. Jour., vol. 31, p. 720–741

Price, W. A. (1947) *Equilibrium of form and forces in tidal basins of coast of Texas and Louisiana*, Am. Assoc. Petr. Geol., Bull., vol. 31, p. 1619–1663

————— (1950) *Saharan sand dunes and the origin of the longitudinal dune: a review*, Geog. Rev., vol. 40, p. 462–465

Rich, J. L. (1942) *The face of South America: an aerial traverse*, Am. Geog. Soc. Spec. Pub., No. 26, 299 p.

Rolland, G. (1881) *Sur les grandes dunes de sable du Sahara*, Géol. Soc. de France, Bull., Trois. Ser., Tome X, p. 30–47

Rossby, C. G. (1943) *Introduction to the conference and some applications of boundary-layer theory to the physical geography of the Middle West*, Conference on boundary layer problems, New York Acad. Sci., Ann., vol. 44, p. 3–12

Rowalt, E. M. (1936) *Anchoring the Clatsop dunes with vegetation*, Soil Conservation, vol. 2, p. 61–63

Saville, Thorndike, Jr. (1950) *Model study of sand transport along an infinitely long, straight beach*, Am. Geophys. Union Trans., vol. 31, p. 555–565

Sayles, R. W. (1931) *Bermuda during the Ice Age*, Am. Acad. Arts and Sci. Proc., vol. 66, p. 381–467

Schott, Gerhard (1935) *Geographie des Indischen und Stillen Ozeans*, C. Boysen, Hamburg, 413 p.

Schumacher, Paul (1874) *Notes on Kjökkenmöddings on the northwest coast of North America*, Smiths. Inst. Ann. Rep., 1873, p. 354–362

————— (1877) *Researches in the Kjökkenmöddings and graves of a former population of the coast of Oregon*, U. S. Geol. and Geog. Surv. of the Territories Bull. 3, no. 1, p. 27–35

Scott, H. W. (1924) *History of the Oregon country*, 6 vols., Riverside Press, Cambridge, Mass.

Seligman, G. (1936) *Snow structure and ski fields*, MacMillan and Co., London, 555 p.

Shepard, F. P. (1948) *Submarine geology*, Harper and Bros., N. Y., 348 p.

Smith, H. T. U. (1940) *Geologic studies in southwestern Kansas*, Univ. Kansas (State Geol. Surv. Kansas), Bull. 34, 212 p.

————— (1945–46) *Sand dunes*, N. Y. Acad. Sci., Trans., Ser. 2, vol. 8, p. 197–199

————— (1949) *Physical effects of Pleistocene climatic changes in non-glaciated areas: eolian phenomena, frost action, and stream terracing*, Geol. Soc. Am. Bull., vol. 60, p. 1485–1516

————— (1951) *Photo interpretation studies in the sand hills of western Nebraska*, Naval Res. Proj., NR 089-016

————— (1954) *Eolian sand on desert mountains* (abstract), Geol. Soc. Am. Bull., vol. 65, p. 1306–1307

Smith, W. D. (1933) *Physiography of Oregon coast*, Pan-American Geologist, vol. 59, p. 33–44, 97–114, 190–206, 241–258

Snavely, P. D., Jr. (1948) *Coquille Formation in the Nestucca Bay quadrangle, Oregon*, Geol. Soc. of the Oregon Country, Geol. News-letter, vol. 14, p. 11–12

Sokolow, N. A. (1894) *Die Dünen; Bildung, Entwicklung, und innerer Bau* (German transl. from Russian 4th ed., 1884, assisted by A. Arzruni), Berlin, Springer, 298 p.

Solger, F. (1910) *Geologie der Dünen, in* Dünenbuch, F. Enke, Stuttgart

Steele, T. A. (1940) *Grass and associated vegetation to reclaim Oregon's coastal sand dunes*, Soil Conservation, vol. 6, p. 43–44

Strahler, A. N. (1952) *Dynamic basis of geomorphology*, Geol. Soc. Am. Bull., vol. 63, p. 923–938

Streeter, V. L. (1948) *Fluid dynamics*, McGraw-Hill Book Co., N. Y., 263 p.

Thompson, W. O. (1937) *Original structure of beaches, bars, and dunes*, Geol. Soc. Am. Bull., vol. 48, p. 723–751

Thornthwaite, C. W. (1931) *The climates of North America according to a new classification*, Geog. Rev., vol. 21, p. 633–655

————— (1948) *An approach toward a rational classification of climate*, Geog. Rev., vol. 38, p. 55–94

Thorp, James, and Smith, H. T. U. (1949) *Map of eolian deposits in North America* (Abstract), Geol. Soc. Am. Bull., vol. 60, p. 1923

Twenhofel, W. H. (1943) *Origin of the black sands of southwest Oregon*, Oregon Dept. Geol. and Min. Industries, Bull. 24, 25 p.

————— (1946) *Mineralogical and physical composition of the sands of the Oregon coast from Coos Bay to the mouth of the Columbia River*, Oregon Dept. Geol. and Min. Industries, Bull. 30, 64 p.

————— (1950) *Principles of sedimentation*, 2nd ed., McGraw-Hill Book Co., N. Y., 673 p.

U. S. Geol. Survey (1945) Map: Geology of northwestern Oregon west of the Willamette River and north of Lat 45° 15′

————— (1954) Surface water supply of the United States 1951, Pt. 14, Water-supply Paper, No. 1218, 332 p.

Walther, J. (1924) *Das Gesetz der Wüstenbildung in Gegenwart und Vorzeit*, Verlag von Quelle und Heyer, Leipzig, 421 p.

Westgate, J. M. (1904) *Reclamation of Cape Cod sand dunes*, U. S. Dept. Agric., Bur. Plant Ind., Bull. 65, 36 p.

EXPLANATION OF PLATES 7–22

PLATE 7.—TRANSVERSE-RIDGE PATTERN IN LOCALITIES 19 AND 20

FIGURE 1.—Active dune belt 7 km south of the Siuslaw River, Locality 20 (see Plate 3, Locality 20). Rudimentary foredune built around driftwood and marram grass, with tongue hills; transverse-ridge pattern in its best development; oblique ridges at right; a remnant of forested dune; a swale in an area reduced to deflation base south of it. Sept. 21, 1940.

FIGURE 2.—North end of Coos Bay dune sheet, Locality 19. Transverse ridges and lee-projections; no foredune, but driftwood and a little marram grass, with tongue hills, at north end; ridges of northern complex (see Plate 3, Locality 19) with small areas not yet stabilized, at right; remnants of forested dunes in open sand. Sept. 21, 1940.

FIGURE 3.—Ground view of zone of transverse ridges, looking north over spit outside Siuslaw River, Locality 20. Aug. 28, 1941.

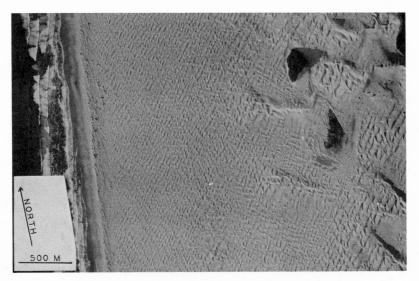

FIGURE 1

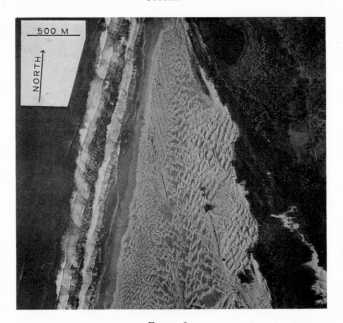

FIGURE 2

FIGURE 3

TRANSVERSE-RIDGE PATTERN IN LOCALITIES 19 AND 20

FIGURE 1

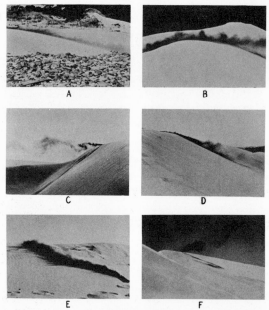

A   B

C   D

E   F

FIGURE 2

FIGURE 3

TRANSVERSE-RIDGE, SURFACE AIR CURRENTS
VISUALIZED BY SMOKE, AND LEE PROJECTION

PLATE 8.—TRANSVERSE RIDGE, SURFACE AIR CURRENTS VISUALIZED BY
SMOKE, AND LEE-PROJECTION

FIGURE 1.—A sinuous transverse ridge with undulating crest and concave slipfaces at high points. Locality 20. July 24, 1940.

FIGURE 2.—Behavior of surface air currents in various situations as visualized by smoke. Enlarged from 16-mm movie frames. A: lee slope of an incipient transverse ridge; the air stream remains attached. B: oblique ridge with rounded summit; separation. C: slipface of mature transverse ridge; vortex layer with sinusoidal profile rolling up. (A perfect vortex formed immediately after this photograph was taken) D: Lee slope of oblique ridge with rounded summit; vortex layer with sinusoidal profile; separation some distance below crest. E: windward slope of an oblique ridge; thick turbulent boundary layer. F: Lee slope of an oblique ridge; separation at sharp crest; a perfect vortex.

FIGURE 3.—Lee-projection with 4 smoke candles demonstrating paths of air currents that form t. Locality 20. Aug. 5, 1940.
i

PLATE 9.—SLOW-MOTION PHOTOGRAPHS OF SMOKE OVER SLIPFACE OF A
TRANSVERSE RIDGE

FIGURE 1.—Sequence from slow-motion picture (64 frames per second). Interval between frames approximately $\frac{1}{10}$ second. *See* text.

FIGURE 2.—*See* Figure 1 and text.

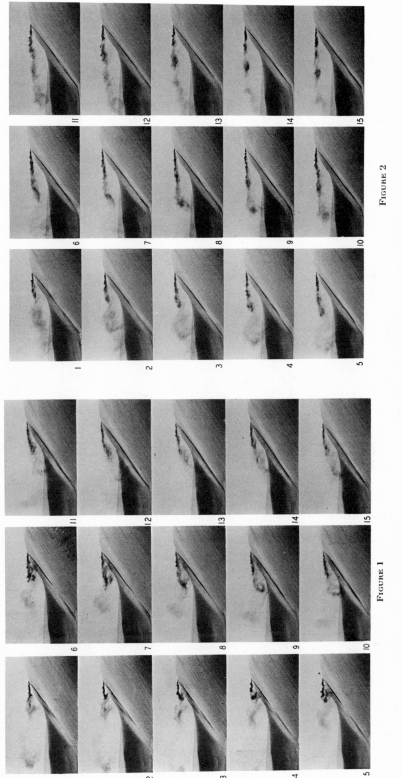

FIGURE 2

FIGURE 1

SLOW-MOTION PHOTOGRAPHS OF SMOKE OVER SLIPFACE OF A TRANSVERSE RIDGE

FIGURE 1

FIGURE 2

FIGURE 3

SAND LIFTED FROM WET BEACH BY WIND, AND
WIND-SCULPTURED DUNE MASS

Plate 10.—SAND LIFTED FROM WET BEACH BY WIND, AND WIND-SCULPTURED
DUNE MASS

Figure 1.—Southward from Sea Lion Point along the shore of Locality 19. The white tongues
on the beach in middle distance are clouds of sand being lifted from the wet surface; incipient transverse ridges farther in. Aug. 3, 1940.

Figure 2.—Sand being lifted from wet beach by wind; picture faces the wind. Same locality and
date as Figure 1.

Figure 3.—Moist dune mass sculptured by wind; effect of structure. Locality 20. Aug. 5, 1940

Plate 11.—TRANSVERSE-RIDGE AND OBLIQUE-RIDGE PATTERNS AT ENDS OF
DRY AND WET SEASONS

Figure 1.—An area of transverse ridges at ends of dry and wet seasons. Locality 20. *A:* Sept. 21, 1940; *B:* April 20, 1941 (initiation of summer pattern).

Figure 2. An area of oblique ridges at ends of dry and wet seasons. Locality 22. *A:* Sept. 21, 1940; *B:* April 20, 1941. The long ridge left of center is *A-A* of Figure 7 and Plate 3, Locality 22

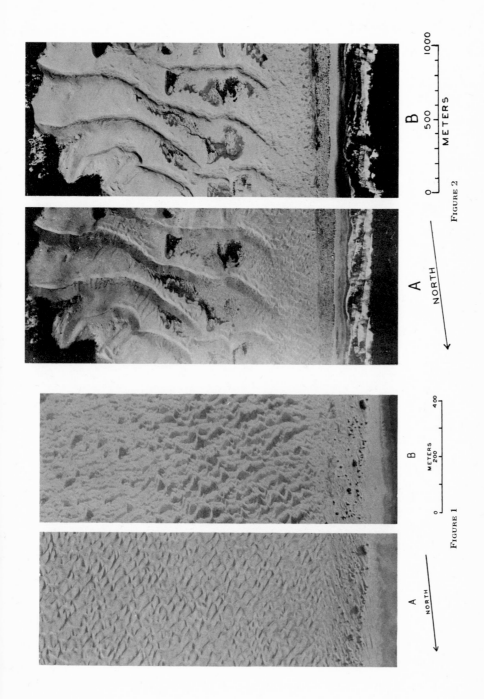

FIGURE 2

FIGURE 1

TRANSVERSE-RIDGE AND OBLIQUE-RIDGE PATTERNS AT ENDS OF DRY AND WET SEASONS

FIGURE 1

FIGURE 2

FIGURE 3

OBLIQUE RIDGES AND PRECIPITATION RIDGE

PLATE 12.—OBLIQUE RIDGES AND PRECIPITATION RIDGE

FIGURE 1.—Mature oblique ridges in Locality 22, looking southeastward. Vegetation in the trough indicates reduction to substratum; the trees in the distance are growing on a remnant of older dunes. Sept. 13, 1941.

FIGURE 2.—Sharp crest of an oblique ridge, looking south-southeastward. An incipient northeast-facing slipface has been formed by an early fall southwesterly wind. Locality 22. Sept. 2, 1941.

FIGURE 3.—Precipitation ridge of outer active ridge system in Locality 23 invading pine forest on deflation plain. At right a youthful oblique ridge. July 15, 1928.

PLATE 13.—OBLIQUE RIDGES AND RUDIMENTARY FOREDUNE

FIGURE 1.—Inner end of an oblique ridge advancing over older forested dunes. Locality 20. July 28, 1940.

FIGURE 2.—A very massive oblique ridge in Locality 20 (A, Plate 3, Locality 20), looking northeastward. The main crest (right) in 1940 rose 49 m above its base. The slipfaces at the left are associated with the fanning out of the ridge and are advancing rapidly southward. The spruce, which projected 12 m at the time of the picture (July 24, 1940) was almost buried in 1948.

FIGURE 3.—A rudimentary foredune built around driftwood and youthful clumps of marram grass. Locality 20. July 24, 1940.

FIGURE 1

FIGURE 2

FIGURE 3

OBLIQUE RIDGES AND RUDIMENTARY FOREDUNE

FIGURE 1

FIGURE 2

FIGURE 3

MATURE FOREDUNE, STAGES ON AN ERODING SHORE, AND
TROUGH BLOWOUT

PLATE 14.—MATURE FOREDUNE, STAGES ON AN ERODING SHORE, AND TROUGH BLOWOUT

FIGURE 1.—Mature foredune built by coalescence of hillocks precipitated by marram grass. Locality 23. Sept. 10, 1941.

FIGURE 2.—Stages in the dune cycle on an eroding shore with meager sand supply. Locality 19. Lower right, at Heceta Beach, stabilized dunes extending to shore, with incipient trough blowouts. Center, various stages in destruction of old forms and building of new: intertrough ridges, young precipitation ridges, deflation areas with pioneer vegetation and with forest. Lower left, sand tongues advancing over low vegetation on a deflation area. Upper right, an older precipitation ridge, its windward slope mantled with transverse ridges; pioneer vegetation advancing behind it followed by forest (area of Plate 15, Figure 1); access to new sand almost cut off. Top of picture, right, terminal ridge of Episode II, mostly stabilized, with patches of still active sand. See also Plate 3, Locality 19. Sept. 21, 1940. The picture, apparently oblique, is actually vertical.

FIGURE 3.—Trough blowout in stabilized dunes, looking inland from near top of beach. Near Heceta Beach, Locality 19. July 29, 1940.

PLATE. 15.—PRECIPITATION RIDGES, EXHUMED FOREST SOIL, AND COMPOUND
SAUCER BLOWOUT

FIGURE 1.—An active precipitation ridge with its associated deflation area; pioneer vegetation followed by pine forest. Locality 19. Sept. 7, 1933.

FIGURE 2.—Slipface of a precipitation ridge invading forest of Douglas fir and Sitka spruce. The trees are 1–1.5 m in diameter. Locality 20, just south of Siuslaw River. Sept. 9, 1941.

FIGURE 3.—An exhumed forest soil layer acting as a temporary deterrent to deflation. In the background the receding windward slope of the precipitation ridge that buried the forest. Locality 19. Aug. 17, 1941.

FIGURE 4.—Compound saucer blowout on windward slope of a precipitation ridge approaching stabilization. Right foreground, older blowout surface partially healed. Locality 19. Sept. 2, 1941.

FIGURE 1

FIGURE 2

FIGURE 3

FIGURE 4

PRECIPITATION RIDGES, EXHUMED FOREST SOIL,
AND COMPOUND SAUCER BLOWOUT

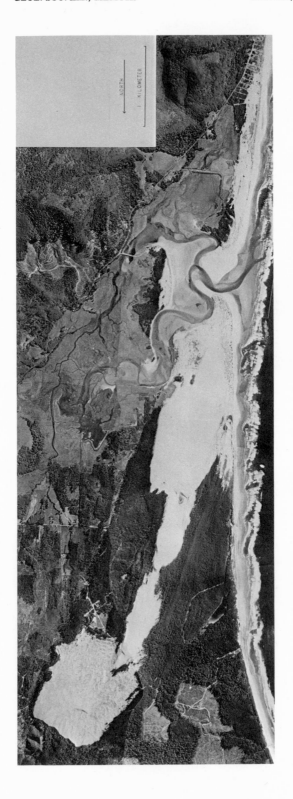

DUNE SYSTEM AT SAND LAKE, LOCALITY 9

PLATE 16.—DUNE SYSTEM AT SAND LAKE, LOCALITY 9

For features *see* Plate 2, Locality 9. Aerophotos by Delano Aerial Surveys, Sept. 20, 1953.

PLATE 17.—CAPE KIWANDA, OBLIQUE AERIAL VIEWS OF LOCALITIES 19 AND 23

FIGURE 1.—Cape Kiwanda (Locality 10) from the south. Seaward-dipping sedimentary rocks; forested remnants of dune system upon them, the one at right showing several old soil horizons. Haystack Rock is just beyond the picture to the left. *See* Plate 2, Locality 10. Aug. 12, 1941.

FIGURE 2.—Southeastward over Locality 19 from a point over its northern extremity; the whole dune complex is shown except its northeast edge. The following features, described in the text and indicated on Plate 3, Locality 19, are visible:

Lily Lake at lower left corner; the northern ridge complex above it, with spots of persistent activity; the two salients of recent invasion, each with successive waves of advance; between them the peninsula of forested dunes with Sutton Creek flowing across its front; next in order southward stabilized dunes extending to shore at Heceta Beach, the Siuslaw River, and Locality 20; at top left the partially rejuvenated precipitation ridges of the eastern system. Photo by Brubaker Aerial Surveys.

FIGURE 3.—Southward over Locality 23 from a point above its northern end. Tenmile Creek in foreground, Coos Bay in background. Eastward from shore: incipient foredune; outer active ridge system; zone of incomplete deflation with remnant masses of older dunes, and lakes in distance; inner active system with conspicuous oblique ridges; marginal stabilized system barely distinguishable. *See* Plate 3, Locality 23. Photo by Brubaker Aerial Surveys.

FIGURE 1

FIGURE 2

FIGURE 3

CAPE KIWANDA, OBLIQUE AERIAL VIEWS OF LOCALITIES 19 AND 23

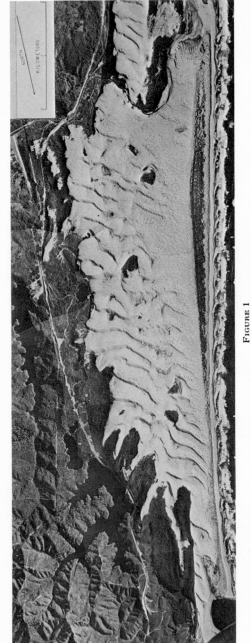

FIGURE 1

FIGURE 3

FIGURE 2

LOCALITY 22: MOSAIC, OBLIQUE AERIAL VIEW, AND FORESTED WAVE-CUT BLUFF

PLATE 18.—LOCALITY 22: MOSAIC, OBLIQUE AERIAL VIEW, AND FORESTED
WAVE-CUT BLUFF

FIGURE 1.—Mosaic covering Locality 22. Umpqua River at north, Tenmile Creek at south;
Clear Lake northeast of dunes, Eel Lake east edge center. Eastward from shore: marram-grass foredune with recently developed deflation strip behind it; zone of transverse ridges; zone of oblique
ridges; parabola complex at north end. *See* Plate 3, Locality 22. Aerophotos by Delano Aerial Surveys, Sept. 18, 1953.

FIGURE 2.—Southeastward from a point near the north end of Locality 22. Parabola complex at
left with several active tongues, the nearest spilling over the forested wave-cut bluff that faces the
sea (*see* Figure 3 of Plate 18); small oblique ridges in front of the bluff. Clear Lake beyond the parabola complex. At right, the oblique-ridge system and remnants of older dunes. Photo by Brubaker
Aerial Surveys.

FIGURE 3.—Forested wave-cut bluff 100 m high where seaward portion of parabola complex of
Locality 22 has been sliced off by sea; spillover from parabola trough behind. In foreground small
oblique ridges; driftwood and newly established marram grass. Sept. 5, 1941.

PLATE 19.—MOSAICS COVERING LOCALITIES 20 AND 21

FIGURE 1.—Middle portion of Locality 21. Tahkenitch Creek and lower end of Tahkenitch Lake at north; south of it, parabola complex built chiefly by summer wind. Threemile Lake at south between dunes and mountain slope. *See* Plate 3, Locality 21. Aerophotos by Delano Aerial Surveys, Sept. 20, 1953.

FIGURE 2.—Mosaic covering Locality 20. Siuslaw River at north, Siltcoos River at south. Cleawox Lake east edge center; west of it deflation area related to its intermittent outlet. Outer zone of transverse ridges, inner zone of oblique ridges; inner portion of forested dunes south of Cleawox Lake not included; an area of artificial stabilization just south of the Siuslaw River. *See* Plate 3, Locality 20. Aerophotos by Delano Aerial Surveys, Sept. 20, 1953.

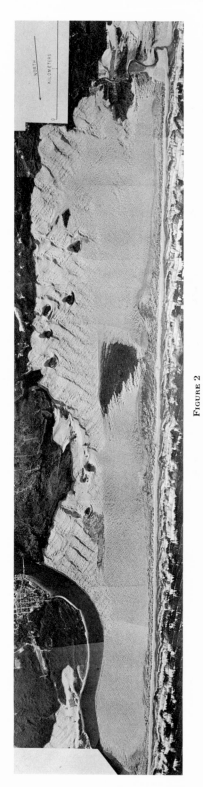

FIGURE 1

FIGURE 2

MOSAICS COVERING LOCALITIES 20 AND 21

FIGURE 1

FIGURE 2

FIGURE 3

REMNANTS OF STABILIZED DUNES, INVASION OF
STABILIZED PRECIPITATION RIDGE, AND SITKA
SPRUCE UNCOVERED AFTER BURIAL

PLATE 20.—REMNANTS OF STABILIZED DUNES, INVASION OF STABILIZED PRECIPITATION RIDGE, AND SITKA SPRUCE UNCOVERED AFTER BURIAL

FIGURE 1.—Remnants of old stabilized dunes surrounded by active sand. Locality 20. Aug. 27, 1941.

FIGURE 2.—Invasion of windward slope of a stabilized precipitation ridge by new sand, as in Figure 12. Burial of forest floor, killing of most of the trees; an occasional survivor. Locality 20. Aug. 9, 1940.

FIGURE 3.—A Sitka spruce which after burial of its base produced large adventitious roots. Such trees provide data for estimation of rate of advance of precipitation ridges. Locality 19. Sept. 2, 1941.

PLATE 21.—CHANGES IN DUNES AFTER 30 YEARS, PERCHED DUNES, AND
OBLIQUE AERIAL VIEW OF LOCALITY 3

FIGURE 1.—Northward from a remnant mass in Locality 23; an interval of 30 years between the
pictures. Photo *A* by T. T. Munger.

FIGURE 2.—Perched dunes, Locality 28. Vigorous erosion has stripped a large area of the terrace surface. Aug. 1, 1925.

FIGURE 3.—Looking northward from point over Long Beach, Washington. Locality 3. Parallel
ridges with bogs and lakes in intervening troughs. Shoalwater Bay and Willapa Bay in distance,
right. *See* Plate 5, Locality 3. Photo by Brubaker Aerial Surveys.

A 1911

B 1941

FIGURE 1

FIGURE 2

FIGURE 3

CHANGES IN DUNES AFTER 30 YEARS, PERCHED DUNES, AND
OBLIQUE AERIAL VIEW OF LOCALITY 3

A

G

F

B

E   D   FIGURE 1   C

FIGURE 2

OBLIQUE AERIAL VIEW OF LOCALITY 4 AND ANCIENT EOLIAN SAND EXPOSED BY
DEFLATION OF RECENT SAND

PLATE 22.—OBLIQUE AERIAL VIEW OF LOCALITY 4 AND ANCIENT EOLIAN SAND
EXPOSED BY DEFLATION OF RECENT SAND

FIGURE 1.—Looking northward from point a short distance north of Gearhart, Oregon. Locality
4. *See* Plate 6.

A: Cullaby Lake at margin, West Lake right center; B: ridge 2, passing east of West Lake; C:
ridge 3; D: ridge 4; E: ridges 5a, 5b; F: Neacoxie Creek with ridge 6 just east of it; G: remnants
of ridges 9a and 9b, with Sunset Lake east of them. Photo by Brubaker Aerial Surveys, 1922.

FIGURE 2.—Ancient eolian sand exposed by deflation among modern dunes. Locality 20. Aug.
30, 1941.

INDEX

S!